SHEEPER

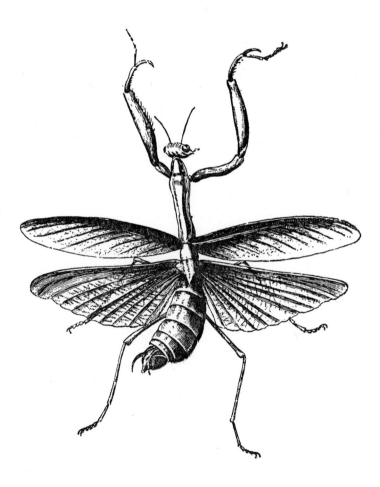

IRVING ROSENTHAL

SHEEPER

"The Poet! The Crooked! The Extra-fingered!"

1967 : GROVE PRESS, INC. : N.Y.

4/1973
Gen.l.

First Printing

Book Designed by Dave Haselwood

Library of Congress Catalog Card No.: 67-20342
Manufactured in the United States of America

CONTENTS

Part One

THE FLOWER CURTAIN LIFTED

MY MOTHER used to whip me with a wooden coat-hanger or with her hand, which I liked better, because it meant that she got some of the sting, too. Her hands were soft and fat like a baby's, with a clear, light skin. My fingers are long, dark, and half-covered with eczema. There is a scar on my left little finger from a bottle opener she threw at me one day. I stood and watched the blood press from the cut and drip on the floor.

Doors locked and unlocked, my stamp book torn in half, my bureau drawers pulled out and dumped on the floor, face always watching me from behind the door frame, and I have to give it a good hard look to make it jump back. And now my white walls change their angles, shift, to move in toward me, slowly, as on a great stage machine, and behind them the green enamelled walls of the kitchen where my mother used to iron late at night, entertaining her boyfriend with the hairy backhands. He would mind me when she was at citizenship class, I can remember him sitting on my bed and showing me a thin pornographic comic book. I remember how the cuffs tightened on the hair of his wrists, and his shirt on the hair of his neck. I remember the feel of hair all over my body.

Chloral hydrate I am yours. I have visions of unearthly

sweet chocolate creams, of a smooth sweet grainless con-
sistency, not coarse or cold like ice cream—a sweetness like
that of lemon ice (not sherbet), which the Romans ate.
Lemon ice from the Apennines. Chloral hydrate has intima-
tions of a perfectly free orgasm—which I've never had, by
the way, because of self-consciousness. I didn't choose chloral
hydrate—it was in a bottle, saw me passing, and winked.
Two weeks ago I was walking down the aisle of a dark, dusty
chemical storeroom, crowded and neat. I saw a brown bottle
full of chloral hydrate, unopened to judge by the dust,
for fifteen years. The crystals are waxy-looking and as heavy
as those of lead nitrate, very soluble, and if you pour a bit of
boiling water on a few of them, when they dissolve lo the
water is icy, like water distilled from a rock—deadly and
chemical—and kept in a horsehoof. It has a harsh taste,
which plagues you up to a minute afterwards. Only someone
who is quite drunk could ever be surreptitiously laid to sleep
by knockout drops, because of this taste. I take chloral hydrate in a slug of raspberry syrup—and feel martyred. About
a teaspoon of the coarse crystals is enough for me, and I
weigh twice as much as most people. A soda cracker is a
good chaser. There is no nausea of any kind, after or in-
between, and if you have a weak stomach like mine (which
could never tolerate peyote) chloral is a blessing.

"Sometimes I'm short." This is what the baker said to me
when I asked for three black-and-whites. "You want a nice
Danish? A prune-cake?" No said I and left. If a man can't
have a black-and-white cookie in the middle of a nice chloral
high, he may as well go back to counting cockroaches or
despairing over all the propositions he was too shy to respond
to. I finally found three black-and-whites in a bakery down
the street. At this bakery they are 3¢ cheaper and I would

say 10¢ worse. On chloral I dig the white vanilla half, which is too sweet for me normally. The chocolate half, just bearable when I'm not under drugs, has a rich and intricate flavor, the first bitter Aztec cocoa to the Spaniards.

The customer before me was an old lady who wanted to know whether the bakery clerk had a bread from yesterday —a white bread, or a rye bread, or a pumpernickel maybe. The clerk looked around until she spotted a small French bread lying alone in a wire basket. A piece of crust had been chipped off one end. "I'll sell you this for ten cents," she said. The old woman looked at her and said, "Will you make it five cents?" Then she looked at me and said, "Everything costs so much." The clerk raised her eyebrows, nodded, and said, "Here, you want to put it in your shopping bag?" The old woman asked her please to put it in a paper bag, if she didn't mind. The clerk put it in one bag, which was too small, and so with a stoical sigh put it in a larger one, folded the top of the bag down neatly, and handed it to the old woman. But she, before putting her nickel into the clerk's hand, asked if the bread was kosher. The answer was, "Oh yes, everything we bake is kosher."

This conversation was conducted in Yiddish. My ability to understand Yiddish increases substantially under drugs, and once under chloral I was able to schmoose briefly with a fruit peddler.

The people I sleep with talk interminably, and pull my prick out of their mouths to think of a new sentence. They say they are not attracted to me, and I allow them the freedom to say this, why I don't know, since in the mirror I have always found myself attractive, excessively so. I have a dark, strong sexual flavor, Jewish or mestizo. To tell the truth, I can only dig my own sexual beauty in the mirror when I see myself by accident—but other people must see me as having

this beauty because they flash eyes at me. In fact I cannot
like anyone who is not attracted to me. There may be no
formal eye-goo but I have to know from some fact like they
are attracted to everyone that I wouldn't be left out. I've
eaten the three black-and-whites now and regret it. Chloral
I love you. Black-and-whites I can do without you—your
high is nauseous and disorienting—though I guess nothing
is easier than to change a few words later and have a narra-
tive out of a drunken lather.

　　Sheeper is a fat man, did things with sheep, and thinks
he's a high liver. Has visits from David and odd house fly
travellers, one as big as a rat, one that David helped him kill,
one walked on his hair (pow pow). He feels bedbugs though
tries not to since cocks and whole minds are at stake. He feels
bad and always hits bottom and keeps finding new bottoms,
and knows queer morticians fix each other up with new dead
trade. He wrestles with deep black angels but never sucked
one since last exposure to a male, now wondering sadly if
he walks around the city giving out love willy-nilly if he'll
ever get some back in return. He sees himself climbing over
ripe bananas (he is only sixteen) but stopped looking at
stars when his boy lust dried up into daydreams of young
men healthily occupied chasing young boys. He admires the
way Piglin eats raw carrots licking his lips so exuberantly he
flips everyone, but envies him only his strange pale orange
lipstick hunger.
　　He has visits from David in flesh but more often in fancy.
Oliver knocks—(hush) thub, thub, thub. Can't think of
David in peace but a vision of Oliver keeps intruding itself.
All right, octopus! little beak nose and blubbery arms. Oliver
has roly eyes and copies his haircomb from a bust of Octavi-
an. Go say you're out of matches, he'll have to light his

cigarette at the stove. He won't, for fear of burning his eye-lashes. There is a film on his mind like cod-liver oil. I wonder if he will miss me and did everything to arrange it. Shaving your armpits, that's going too far Queen's Footman. Rubber swimfins and a silver chain around his neck. . . . I see David in a withering snowstorm, face of a Scandinavian, powdery traps of snow in the air. An Eskimo is carving his face, cutting out neat semicircular strips of flesh which he throws to the birds. The face is a mask of stone and blood. Leave me not, mask, to the bloody eyes of Oliver waiting for me underwater. He came on as a fish queen but I got his number. Suffering eyes and black arms, wavering in the undertow.

While I wear shirts until they smell quite bad, and long after the cuffs and collars are dirty, I cannot walk barefoot across a room without lifting my toes high into the air. And once I reach my destination I do what I can to brush the dirt from the soles of my feet. For I live in a dust of cockroaches I am loath to disturb—bits and pieces, a ragged leg, an empty egg case, a whole insect flat and dry as a pressed leaf, a delicate tan wing flutters, a black ribboned abdomen hollow as the leg of a crab, a whole insect dry and light as a ghost floats to the ground. But don't go away for I will give you a vision of David and then secrets so powerful I may be stung dead by black bees and red beetles before I can tell them (beetles knock themselves against the wall like flying trucks, the lamellas come to life like mine detectors). And the trouble has begun already. You may not believe me, but directly I wrote that last long sentence, a play of sirens that was never heard on this earth came in through the window to distract me or frighten me—and I felt hairs on my left leg moving. But on.

2

DAVID

HE SAID he had a bad headache and went into the bedroom to lie down. He has an unfulfilled passion for sixteen-year-old boys. He is a big intellectual, jabbering words at a psychoanalytical convention. And this poor dear roommate of his who has lived with him for three years, suffered his eccentricities, against whom he has tested reality as he puts it, roommate who does the cooking, buys groceries (I came over to pick up my spades), you know what he said about this here roommate, on the occasion of meeting my fifteen-year-old teahead friend, whom I found sitting on an ashcan, lower east side, one mouth where it should be and two more for eyes? He said "I would leave my roommate for him." So lustful he flipped three nembutals down his gullet, and went into the bedroom to lie down and masturbate. Thinking to be awakened by the teahead.

Sleep sounds draw me in gliding—like a drugger watching his victim asleep. He is supine, motionless, dead asleep with his head thrown back, a single throat vessel pulsing. You think you can see his blood waiting to burst into his skin—which is blue, white, and red at once. He cuts himself when shaving, milk flows out. After a moment it turns brilliantly red. He has the complexion of Death alive.

So you hold a conversation, tortured and imaginary, while

David is sleeping. Death says, "If it wasn't David it would have been Death, and if it wasn't Death it would have been a kind of terrestrial Oliver." His Death is frail and forced. I love him awake and asleep, and will maintain his body—beautiful big hands and feet, and he fidgets hugely with his hands—and frail spirit. He keeps those hands all folded, and when he drops to sleep they open up slowly like wings. He has a splinter of an ego he says. But the splinter is all egotist I think.

He scoreth with hustlers one time apiece only, visions of love and skin, sweet confidence, flat noes. Brown hair with a flush of red. Sad, frustrated silence. I love you leaf-hoppers, lace-wings, wasps, May-flies, fly-hawks.

A tiny mosquito lights on David's arm. It gets tangled in arm hairs, struggles to free itself, gives up and falls over dead. Its tiny legs close like lashes. David says, with half-opened eyes, and rather too late I think, "Don't come near me humming mosquito, suck up the cats."

I go to sleep now without two handkerchiefs for my come, a box of kleenex for my sinus, and a pair of pajamas to make me believe someone cares for me all over. I let the sheets go four weeks without changing because my dreams are never neat and clean no matter how or where I sleep. My blankets are always in a pile, which I flatten out a little before throwing over me, and I never tuck them under my mattress, for why should I let my bed embrace me or my pillow clasp my cheek? Beds are for young Prousts, not old men like me. David has pressed sheets and half-clasped rosary-carrying hands. He is clean-shaven, young, benign, and whispers. He wears sandals and a long robe. He is tonsured and has thoughts like this: "Am I growing too fat for my white homosexual swimming trunks?"

He lays photographs on me. "This is the way I looked when I was nineteen." I am supposed to say, "You haven't changed a bit." I say, "You look essentially the same." "Essentially the same. I should think so." He is offended because he uses twenty-eight Helena Rubinstein lotions to look exactly the same.

3

GLIMPSES OF DAVID AT AN
AMUSEMENT PARK AND ON 42ND STREET

EERWIG'S LAUGH OF DEATH, skeletons clacking along
mechanically, wondering when their bones will wear
out, now and then buttonholing strollers on the boardwalk
with a tale as sad and nasty as I've heard (the voice is badly
recorded, a hum is in the background, there are plenty of
clicks and scratches, and before the voice begins there is a
loud shrill feedback swell): "Friends, I was once as you are
now, wearing a cloak of veins and blood and membranes
thick and thin. I longed as ye do now to perish. I longed
for death the length of my life, which was short, and therefore I felt gratitude, or rather satisfaction, on my deathbed. I
was sold to an eminent physick professor, who threw a handful of corpse-beetle (Dermestidae) grubs into my wash-tub
coffin, and they made short shrift of my flesh. His students
washed my bones, sorted and shellacked them, and put me
together with wires. I knocked around for a century and lost
nothing more than a few phalanges and metacarpals, and my
skull developed the large crack that you can see. I have been
re-wired five times and am now owned, along with my com-
panions, by the House of Thrills, which is just left of yon exit
from the boardwalk. Each day I am given fifty wild jiggles,
and (at last) I am fracturing rapidly, quite splintering away.
Thus it has taken me over a hundred-and-twenty-five years

(if only the House of Thrills employs me until I am utterly useless) to witness the dissolution of my body—and I consider myself lucky. Friends, provide for your cremation before you die. And visit the House of Thrills." David said "There is such a thing as inoffensive advertising" and turned to walk away. But I was in his path. Rather than bump into me he pushed me in my chest with his fingers. I was hurt but said nothing.

He slowed to a stop by the plate glass window of a cafeteria. A short glance behind him, then the long sweep of an automatic calculator casting up a product digit by digit. He turned his hand to his sunglasses, a motion of such gentleness that it could only be made with fingers water-logged and the fingernails cut close. He hardened those fingers to poke me in the ribs.

We are walking down the street and he leaves me suddenly. Where is he? Talking to a boy. I stop and wait for him, ten feet away. He does not call me. Suddenly a torrent of people passes. They look at me disapprovingly, wonder what I am waiting for. I am desperate. I move two feet closer. He turns around, sees me, comes toward me. It is clear he has not finished with the boy, who in the meantime walks to the curb to whisper something in the ear of an older man. "I'll meet you at the car," says David. "The keys," I say. He does not respond (afraid I will drive the car away). I throw my hand down (forget it), turn around and walk away. At the car I sit on the fender. The crowd continues passing. I set my face firmly in its direction (also the direction David will come), my eyes are blurred, I am paralyzed. I pretend that several people walking toward me are David, though I know they are not. Does he come? Does a policeman ask me to move? (I am in the kitchen with my mother and her boyfriend. It is night, she is ironing, the rest of the house is dark.

A long shadow of light falls into the hall. Someone seizes my legs and pulls me slowly from the kitchen into the hall. I scream "Mama, Mama, help me." She is behind an invisible glass wall, ironing and talking to her boyfriend. I am pulled down the hall. No one responds to my screams, or makes any indication that they have been heard. I am pulled into the black bedroom without the solace even of knowing I was being ignored.)

These are the glimpses of a mind digesting itself—herself I should say. These are the fat lachrymal thoughts of a cat eating her kitten.

4

COOPS

THE TAXI DRIVER said, "There's been real progress in the field of mental health, I remember thirty, forty years ago we kids wouldn't go near the hospital."

Yellow ice on the ground, glass doors, the stench of the ward. How can I touch the smoke-stained fingers? Absolute vulnerability. Talking through space to the absolute bottom. The hearing of your own voice echo back. Eat some of your Hershey. The utter starry beauty which comes surplussing to the defense where the teeth are missing. The blue eyes and broken blackheaded nose. The brownskin eyelids and all the silver glamour of mascara and eye shadow remembered. Remember half a mouthful of teeth are missing. Touch the ones that are left. Everything will be completed.

I am sorry to report that whenever Roy or Huncke find themselves growing grim about the mouth they knock people's hats off to end up in jail, and they are never entirely happy unless they are prisoners. And the same is true for David and the Poet with respect to looney bins. Whether it is masochism or the need for total protection or an attempt to exercise the human spirit by self-imposed adversity, I know not. Take the case of Roy.

Here I have a pilot's thumb, here Roy, here boy. Roy you showed me how to wear shades. Roy you said this is David.

Roy you want to be arrested again, otherwise you wouldn't
smoke pot in the street. How you thrived in prison. You
want to give up your marriage scene out here in the city and
go back to your jailboy, "Rimbawd". You want to put your
hand on his ass under the guard's nose and say, "Hows about
some cunt, baby?" Is that it? You want to make all the prepa-
rations again, time the guard's round, hide the blankets, lay
them out on the floor, a marriage bed two thicknesses of
blanket high, undress completely, dig "boy-flesh is girl-flesh"
and the blond down on Rimbawd's sweet chest. Here in the
city your lovers are all women but your friends are all fairies.
The American guilt machine still has you pinioned. You
take infinite pains to discover the disposition of my time after
you and your wife left me with David. Roy you *want* me to
do what I want, and what could make me love you more? My
love's advice is to make it with your Wife, turn her into a boy
if necessary, but stay out of jail. For if you go back to the
penitentiary, who will watch out for me then, and who will
be pleased by my maneuvering? Skinny poet Roy. Your Wife
was taking a pee. Suddenly the sound stopped. It started
coming from the cat, who was sitting outside the bathroom
door. Suddenly the sound came from outside the front door.
Your Wife felt like screaming, but at least succeeded in
opening the front door. It was David.

All your Davids have the most interesting patter, and why
I can't hear it just by hanging around ice-cream parlors I
cannot understand.

I am not literary. It's just a hundred false starts each time
you cross my mind, like a lion coming out of its lair,
growling to and fro and then dipping back inside. The start
of I love you, the start of suicide, the start of destroying my
letters for fear I will be hospitalized again, the start of I must
have chloral, company, seeds of marijuana. . . . Water instead

of grapefruit juice, one cruller not two, say take care! and slam the door of your car instead of touching your wrist and then the weakest slam and through the window a milky goodnight.

I wouldn't love you so much if I didn't see you on the floor, diabetic, drooling, a handsome young man of twenty-two shaved by the attendants (all this in *Macbeth*). Not only did they shave you, but the nurse gave you a daily injection of insulin. (An overdose and you fell into a coma but came out of it sane, and that is the origin of insulin shock therapy.) You would think that shaving a man is like washing his feet, but nothing can make attendants lay down their pride (they rode the mental hospital circuit from Galveston to Raleigh, on a series of discharges for cruelty). They cursed you, shoved you, pulled you up, and one attendant hit you. I cannot understand why it upset them so much to see you just give up, so directly and physically. You just crumpled to the floor, your eyes crossed and wandering, you drooled and tried to say a few words, but I could not understand them. I think you pissed in your pants. I fell in love with you.

This is the way it should have been: I had all your clothes taken off, and diapers put on you. I gave you wooden cars to play with. I sat with you on the strong dayroom sofa (you weigh 180 pounds). I dandled you and held you in my lap. You got a hard-on. I wanted to blow you, and did. You responded immediately. I loved you in this way for several weeks, and you me, until we were sane.

This is the way it was: They took off all your clothes but your shorts and threw you into seclusion. I walked around the grounds until I passed below your window. You pressed against the grille, your soft genitals peeking from your shorts. You begged me in Spanish to telephone your brother. You promised me twenty-five dollars. Ah David, you threw yourself from despair into hope, and what could I do? They said I was making you sicker, and moved me to another ward. I went crying, because you had offered me money.

And the great big-breasted lady attendant who used to bring used Loot Magazines for her patients to read, isn't that enough to make you cry? Or the attendant always writing letters, trying to organize a professional society of attendants, and to change the name to psychiatric aide? Or the bounties and favors which flowed from the hands of one or two others, enough to snag you, tackle you is more like it, "no, I don't know any 'psychophysical methods,' if they want to stab me with a pencil or strangle me, my philosophy is let them, my life isn't so pure and good that I don't deserve it." Thoughts like this make my hair stand on end. And my prick too, and let's get it out quite firmly here and now, that the only love that can possibly thrive in an institution or anywhere else is love of the flesh. And I'm sick of apologizing for a whole series of hard-ons, with which I edified the children of my Sunday School classes. Let it stand, let this sentence be.

David seven years old burst into the door frame, delirious, looking for me, face chapped from the hike to Church. And when our eyes met it was Heaven.

Delirious is not exact enough. David's face was more than chapped, it was red with anger (stop *screaming,* you'll have your bottle in a *minute,* dear God make that baby stop screaming). But his features were composed, dead serious in fact, in fact slightly contorted. His eyes moved rapidly from one face to another. When his eyes struck mine he swept to me, and I stooped over to embrace him. He was too excited to know what to do or say. While I held him about the waist, he slowly offered me a little booklet he had made from construction paper. His hand was trembling. He placed his other hand, incredibly hot, on my cheek. Half a minute later he was talking loudly with a cluster of his classmates.

SKIN

CHLORAL HYDRATE or any depressant, and that peculiar drug marijuana, are all bad for my skin. The depressants uninhibit my urge to scratch (sleep does this too, and I have gone to bed in gloves), while marijuana intensifies the itch. And, like a microscope, resolves the itch—that is, makes it so specific, that I have scratched an area of skin raw no bigger than the pupil of an eye. I understand Huncke and all uncontrollable habits because of my itching and scratching. I join hands with the whole human race.

The sound of scratching in the garbage pail. Two prep school mice in blazers are picketing the garbage-collecting industry for its growing efficiency. One carries a placard which reads: Down with Batshit's and Whitefish's Scavenger Association. The placard of the other reads: Hurrah for poets who squeak! Wieners! McClure! Lamantia! Corso!

Try to cross out the sound of scratching. So you go to a dermatologist and he shrugs his shoulders, lifts up a pant leg and shows you his eczema even worse than yours. "We are all specialists in the disease we are suffering from," he sighs. "Don't lay any of your poopy old aphorisms on me," I shot back.

Will someone come by, David (I have a better chance of seeing Piglin spring up from these pages) or God knows who, and stay with me awhile, a week, a month, sleep with me, give the time to me, and if I start scratching take my hands away, keep my mind occupied with a jabbering cock or your whole biography? Oliver, how did you seep in? And because in my extremity I have the twisted strength to spurn an old sincere if somewhat fishy suitor—ah the rat or crab a human heart is!—I deserve only the debris that I'm left with, scabs and exfoliations and scratches and itchings and watchings of cockroaches walking up on the wall. Surface things, always nick-nick-nibble, and always too much light in your eyes. This is a true pot fact, dig it. What could be more important for Sheeper than learning that little fact, his love for David is silly too.

Now eczematous skin is extremely erogenous (note use of the double augmented effect at the twenty-third bar of the theme). Erogenous, what will that boy think of next. Really it is. And I'll give you a few tips and clues on how to manufacture an orgasm without a David, with nothing but a hot shower: give yourself a case of eczema, poison oak will do. The spray should be fine and very hard, the water hot, the adjustment delicate. Direct a light warm spray on the affected area, and slowly turn the water knob at approximately the same speed as the sensation of pleasure increases. If you turn the knob too fast you will scald yourself, but a skin getting its kicks won't let itself be burned. Stick with the pleasure and you're safe. You can achieve a mighty fine orgasm without an erection this way or you can let yourself go and have an erection. And there is nothing better for a prose style than stroking a dry eczema for a few minutes each day. If you scratch it you will end up writing for Loot.

Hey Puck, thought of Oliver stroking my hair makes me shiver. He tries to find something charming in it—a straight, coarse, natural beauty. A real schmuck. I let my hair grow

an inch and will have more waves than a Bickford queen.
And the only reason he can't tell this from such of my hair
he sees—and there are plenty of clues—is his own wavy
hair. Vain, vain Oliver, squirting out ink like an octopus.
My ringlets are tighter than his are. . . . I cover all my beauties, short hair and always wear socks. Shades for the Near
Eastern eyes and very, very loose pants.

David has gone now, art should be beautiful. The vision
of David is over, nothing remains but to fold open secrets.

That all these things, one acting on the other, marijuana
and chloral, my starvation, the appearance and vision of
David, a Persian divan given to me by a young lady (also a
novelist) have opened a vein in my head. Call it a C.V.A. or
sweet upset in my blood. A bus shifting gears excites me as
much as English prose style, great plastic language, my great
printed inheritance.

There is nothing I want this memoir to resemble more
than a skin disease. Lay that on art should be beautiful,
Sheeper, Jewish schmuck.

MOTHER

MY MOTHER'S SLAP was an ugly concussion which drank in my throat, chest, and entrails like a black pelican sipping. I can still see the room forming about me again, in waves of bottle-bottom horror. My frightened reflexes whispered "At least hide your head in your arm," but if I tried, my mother would scream "Don't dare raise your arm against your own mother, is that what I sent you to Hebrew School for, to learn the Fifth Commandment?" and she would slap me again even harder. Not long ago someone really slugged me (breaking my jaw). I came to on the sidewalk thinking she was at me again.

My whole childhood was a mad race around the dining-room table to avoid falling into her hands. At most I delayed the beating for a few minutes, and my sad and desperate hope was that someone would ring the front door bell. One day, in a fit of anger, she unbolted the door and threw me out. I fled three thousand miles without stopping and for years afterwards strained at the west edge of the continent ready to plunge into the Pacific and beyond it if ever she picked up my trail. Still I wake up each morning in terror.

She used to bonk me with a wooden mallet. "Stop hitting me Mama, me your young son Sheeper. I beg you to stop hitting me." In time to the blows: "I beg you! I beg you! I beg

you! I beg you! I beg you!" And then silently: "Now look
what you've done. My friends in the tenement will stroke
their index fingers at me, chanting 'Shame, shame, beggar,
beggar.' O.K. black Mama, I will never light a candle in
your memory and if I see one lit I will blow it out." Is it any
wonder that I sit quietly at parties, or that women find me
aloof?

My mother never caught my imagination from the outside,
like everyone else I think about. She was there from the inside, sitting. Sitting or standing at the sink in her Madame
Bat costume, waiting for an eight-quart pot to fill up. Or sitting on my bed, cleaver in hand, reading my comic books.
She is the very model of a modern career woman just flown
back from hemstitching to cook her little family dinner. She
imagines we may not appreciate the sacrifice she is making to
cook at all, and turns to us, snarling "Vat's wrong mit good
plain American boiled chicken?"

Now the fox is a notoriously seductive and sex-hungry animal and in the absence of a suitable partner will assume
human shape just to get laid. Both genders assume the shape
of women—it is men they lust for. But the genders differ, in
that the vixen always tries to lead its human mark through
sex and passion to his doom, while the male fox just wants
the fuck and other harm than this it does not do.

Go try to get an honest urine specimen from a woman.
Even under the strictest medical surveillance she will manage to slip in a drop of perfume. Women kill the luster of
the jewels they wear, always buying more marvelous rings
to wear the magic out of, while we have to wear plain ugly
ones just to ease our finger. All fingers I ever heard of long
for a ring or a beautiful strap to carry.

Give me a lace-wing or a snake-fly to a woman any day.

Give me those beautiful, big, red metallic eyes, overcast with gold, give me a chartreuse body and soap-film wings, with a sheen of lilac or blue sky. Give me that clumsy flutter or the short walk on the wall. Give me the wilted antennae, Death already at the tips. Finally the antennae curl like a moth's tongue, and the pale body shrivels.

Have you ever seized an outraged moth and uncurled its tongue with a pin? Unfolded the inner wing of a grasshopper, clear fan dipped in ink? Held a kidnapped tree frog on your finger like a ring?

I am tired of being laid by women and would rather wake up in the claspers of a giant moth than in fat human thighs. The last time I slept with a woman she laid me on my back, squatted on top of me, stuffed a small penis inside of her, she accidentally stuffed in a few other things too, and proceeded to bounce up and down for ten minutes. I could have been a Coca-Cola bottle, it would have made no difference to her. In fact I don't like the idea of *fucking* anything. I am willing to be corrected in this matter, but if you can't have an orgasm simply by touching the naked body of your beloved, don't you think you ought to get yourself someone else? After two years my first analyst moved to Honolulu. I was able to start with the second right at the point I had left off with the first.

I look like a sheep. I have the big overgrown body of a child, for no one held me for anything better than to squirt a few seeds in me (sob) or on me, or to lay me back and treat me like a Coca-Cola bottle (sob sob)—and the men have been more tender than the women. Women, stay away. Put down this book, it's not for you. I can see you pressing it to your crotches. My mother gave me such a dose of herself I am forever immune to your blandishments.

Females! If you only knew how virulent my mother was, you would start eating testosterone like candy. You would overrun Denmark screaming "Rip out my organs! Rip out my organs!" You would chop off your heads.

Am done with the greedy witches who will take hammer and bathrobe and never return them. Witch! witch! witch! witch! witch! I wish I could jump right off this page and scream witch in your ear if you are a female. Stop reading this book!

7

X

TRUE THERE ISN'T much to be said for the company of misogynists. Professor X is the worst of them all, and even I was shocked by the poison syrup he kept feeding Charles's wife in Carmel. But more of that later.

In his youth Professor X was a suffragette for the rights of homosexuals. He is ready to suck out my juices and watches me fixedly. His eyelids droop. His face is erect, the skin drawn tight. He has pulled his dewlaps down below his shirt collar, so his neck is long and thin like a turkey's. His smile is such as might be arranged by an embalmer. He thinks he has the right to dangle his flabby old man's malice at whomever he likes. He argues only by evasion and deflection, and, called on it he asks for an instance, and if one is given he diverts attention to it, maybe challenging the memory of his conversant and then maybe changing the subject to memory itself. The quick backtrack way he puts me down, not openly, like an old demon fox.

The quality David and Professor X have in common—I can't think of a word to describe it—the Northern Lights have disordered my brain—that quality of drinking themselves silly while talking to you, as at a cocktail party, except you are not drinking at all. As if they were freeloading, but it is their own whisky. Professor X pretends his right arm is a waiter at the Club 21 pouring champagne like water. The word is "expansive." David giggles about his escapades with hustlers, oblivious to my jealousy. X fills another tumbler with whisky and rambles on about Shakespeare and Oxford. Meanwhile the fire is flashing orange on the windowframe and I can see flickers in the black sky outside. Fuck X and his Famous Queer Histories, I rush out of the house to see pale green streaks wavering and the whole sky a dust cloud of light. There I see a single ray to some Bethlehem racing, and here is a smear of black Inky Way. Here is a pale glow like over a city and here are the green fingers of light in the sky, playing and shifting like searchlights or organ pipes, now a spiral, now a staircase, now an avalanche of light. The sky is all white in full voltage. Over my head a dome hole forms, like a black Maltese cross. I lift mine arms and cause the Northern Lights to glow and spiral with my magic finger.

8

UNDER WATER

SUDDENLY THE LIGHTS were blinding, and I said to our host (he supplied the cigarette papers), "Either turn off the light or I will put on my shades." He turned off the light, the jellyfish, which annoyed me, so I put on my shades. I cannot describe how obliging this host was. I sneezed once or twice when we first came in, and he turned on the air conditioner. Later we kept trying to persuade him to shut it off, since we hated to see all that smoke going to waste, but he was determined to remove whatever in the air had made me sneeze. What he was trying to remove was the smoke, the jellyfish. In the middle of the third joint my socks slipped into my shoes and walked to the door. Everyone asked where I was going. I jerked my thumb toward Roy, said "He knows," and sailed out of the house.

I reached the street, the corner, glanced at the intersection signpost (I never forget to do this, and I've sailed into the open from a dozen strange houses), and walked fifty blocks overcome by the fear of death. I dreaded passing anyone for fear they would think I was stoned, and I passed a parked patrol car and did all I could to walk along the crack in the pavement. On the sidewalk a stark chalk outline of a female torso. Big hips, breasts, and a bisected vulva. Frighteningly heterosexual. (What's happening to our younger generation? In my youth the dirty pictures were phalluses almost exclusively, and they were drawn by boys under the heaviest social pressure not to go queer—and poor scapegoats like me bore the brunt of this pressure: the same boys who used to draw cocks called me a fairy when I walked down the street.) But then by a kind of grace I noticed a cock drawn in softer chalk, pointing to the vagina.

When I reached the corner, I saw the patrol car following me out of the corner of my eye, and I panicked. The same thing happened on my trip to Salinas, exactly. I was driving a car rather fast and not very well, and was more or less keeping on the right of the white line in the middle of the road. I had no license and had done very little driving. I saw a highway patrol car parked on the road ahead, and I became so nervous that my car weaved back and forth across the white line. I breathed a bit more easily when the patrol car had been left behind, but soon I saw it in the rear-view mirror, and it forced me to stop. I very nearly crashed into the mountainside. I was now certain that I had been wobbling, and wondered if there were any blood test for pot. Suddenly the patrol car turned into a taxicab, and I turned the corner and ducked into a doorway. Ten minutes later I ducked into a luncheonette and said, "Two Milky Ways, please." I felt in full empathy the panic of the proprietor and two customers seeing me shades and unshaven. Their bodies unjelled at the sound of two nickels on the counter. The proprietor was so relieved that he ran to the candy shelf, shouted "Yes sir, two Milky Ways coming right up," seized the bars and came from behind the counter to deliver them to me, in person so to speak. During the rest of my death-walk I kept taking off my dark glasses and looking into plate glass windows to see if my pupils had contracted. Sometimes when I walk on the street I feel like an intruder on the space and air of other people, but in a pot high I believe the sidewalks *belong* to them, and that they want me off their portions as soon as possible. That is why I walk so fast.

Is that you, Sheeper, trying to pass yourself off as a teahead? As I live and breathe. Get to bed this minute, and don't forget to wash your hands and face. A teahead. And don't wash half the dirt off and wipe the rest off on the towel, wash it all off. God in Heaven what can we expect from that boy next. It's them books he reads all day long, them lousy books. One week he thinks he's a homosexual, and the next week he's a teahead. Sheeper? Do I hear the water running? He's an outcast that kid.

Or:

Vat's all dat, I don' understan'. It must be somethin' bad, I'll kill 'im. Sheeper, you doity bastard, vat you been up to? I slave all day mit da vashin' an' arnin' an' you run aroun' all day mit dose lousy friends of yours, bums. Get in da house. I'll cripple you. Get in da house right now, you son of a bitch. I'll kill you. . . . Take off your pants.

Which mother would you rather have? Which do you think Sheeper had? What do you think Sheeper's mother did when she found a box of rubbers in Sheeper's drawer? What do you think Sheeper's mother did when she found a box of rubbers in her own drawer? And where is Sheeper's father anyway? Does he have any paternal function besides holding Sheeper occasionally when the mother wants to beat him—I mean holding him so that he can't run away, not holding him to protect him? (The only person who ever protected Sheeper was Aunt Ida, no blood relation you may well imagine; not so David—I thought we were through with him—who always managed to attract a few protectors among the older boys. In this class we may place Sheeper.)

Sheeper's mother didn't say a word, but the abuse she hurled at him took a new form. Suddenly Sheeper found himself a whoremaster, a chippy-chaser—Sheeper, who had never seen any woman besides his mother naked (she was ugly enough),—Sheeper, who had already assigned himself the role underneath when he and his boyfriends played fucking.

Sheeper had both little hands on the edge of his mother's sacred drawer, open, his nose just above it. Silver napkin rings and the smell of amber, lace handkerchiefs, an embroidered box filled with rose leaves, a karakul collar, letters from Europe, two red velvet ring-boxes, a phial of smelling salts, starched men's shirt collars in a black lacquered box (gold cranes wading, fish flickers in the water, Fujiyama), a chamois nail buffer, a crystal perfume bottle with silver cap, a blue box of rubbers. Sheeper's mother put her hand around the blue box and dropped it into her apron pocket. She gently unpeeled his fingers and shut the drawer. On any other day she would have rapped them with her knuckles. Or she would have suddenly shut the drawer without warning him. (I don't care what you do to my fingers, but I will take your bat wings and silk harpy armbones and snap them like sticks. *Leave David alone, witch.*)

Sheeper's mother had many illnesses, but the one thing she never did was rush to the window and throw up outside (dig that, witch next door, and learn some manners before bitching about how I treat my parrot). However, she never flushed the toilet after pissing, and while Sheeper was reluctant to pull the chain before he pissed—the noise of rushing water used to upset him (ordinarily he flushed the toilet just before closing the bathroom door behind him)—still he was more reluctant to mix his urine with his mother's.

9

PIGLIN

"WOMEN WALLOWING to the water hole. Humph!" grumped Piglin, thigh-watching pretty pink coeds trot to the swimming pool. The ramshackle buildings of the old Girls' Gymnasium were the opera of which Piglin was phantom. The janitor would find a ladder missing and assume Miss Tush was using it for a new calisthenic. The girls had even stopped squealing at an occasional squawk or rustle under the shower-room floor—"Pish, little sillies, it is only a skunk." And every time Piglin saw cunt, he would finger his tight little asshole and chuckle, "I got hair too there," and in the shower a girlish finger would drop to a secret tiny hard-on and press it once or twice like a button there with the water running all over, and soon something would force its way between Piglin's fly buttons (on these carefully planned excursions he never wore underwear), up to the floorboards and through a crack, slither across the shower-room floor (gently bumping, recoiling, and skimming over strips of green rubber mat laid down to protect the girls' feet from splinters), and crawl right up into the girl's cunt, while she with eyes raised pretended to soap under her arms.

"The view from below has much to recommend it," he told me confidentially, one day when the two of us were in the Boys' Shower Room alone. So saying, he hung his wet

31

towel on his cock, to show that even soft it was always half
stiff. As the towel slid to the floor, he posed like the Discus
Thrower. Sheeper looking up quickly looked down, up the
ladder and down, I think I detected a bat of those Near
Eastern eyelashes. I posed like the Lizard Killer. Come on
Sheeper, lizards are a dime a dozen. Piglin *wants* you to look
at him, he pivoted toward you. Walnut in a nest of wet
brown hair. The cock is circumcised, long, bright pink, and
curves to the left. Think of it with a hard-on (the boys are
fifteen).

Grotto, an underground club belonged to by Piglin and
Sheeper, now there alone, time several months after the
shower. All the boys own funny hats. Piglin's eyes are above
the ground, rooting in wet, dirty leaves. His heels are on a
ladder, his elbows are resting on the trapdoor frame. He has
absently unzipped his fly, pulled his cock out through the
double trap of his briefs—and there it stands, long, rubbery,
and free-swinging, pulsing and rising. He looks at it and says,
"Hey Sheeper, blow me." Sheeper is beside himself. Piglin
does not take his own proposal too seriously, nuzzles his
snout (as he will) in the crook of his arm, and abuses himself. He crosses his arms (why I always gotta pull myself off,
well I refuse). *"Come* on, Sheeper." Sheeper is ready to faint.
The only thing he has presence of mind to do is ring-toss a
black bowler hat on Piglin's cock.

Books borrowed from Sheeper a late-maturer by Piglin a
handsome young early-maturer, blond down on his face and
a pocket full of dirty stories, he gives you one to read, fifth
carbon folded up, watches you closely and says, "Well, do
you have a hard-on?"—books borrowed from Sheeper as a
big brain-eyed child by Piglin who never carried books to
class, and Piglin has the neck cords and large hands of a
man, blond down on his face, hand in his pocket to cover

an erection, the smell of a fart about him—books borrowed from Sheeper not as you thought to be read, but at the end of class to cover Piglin's erection.

Piglin's face was at one end of the range which goes from handsome young pig with short snout-nose to jowly capitalist swine who roots in plenty of old, clothy, wet dollar bills and female substances. Partial out Piglin's youth, still David would want to squirt pearl-juice on him because he resembled a pig (all boys who look like animals are beautiful—squirrels, rats,—rats fart—monkeys, horses, rabbits—rabbits let themselves be fucked in the ass, though sometimes they tell mother). The problem is, Muse, that Sheeper was blind to the beauty of any animal with fewer legs than six, and, as David, has to dig Piglin for porcinity. Muse: Let Sheeper be Jewish and Piglin excitingly *traif* (Sheeper's mother would never have liked Piglin). One tosses and turns to try to figure out what Piglin's cock feels like (cock of a pig), without actually putting one's hand into his fly (the zipper is cold) and with some trouble through the double trap of his briefs. You can bet that Piglin would help out by putting his hands behind his head and thrusting his pelvis forward. Piglin took advantage of any friendly tussle to rub himself back and forth until he came.

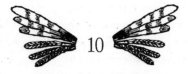

10

THE LETTER TO BRIAN

DEAR BRIAN:
    David invites you to live with him when you move to Salinas. He is willing to support you without touching you —if that is what you want (David was born in Madras). He will put no pressure on you, he is constitutionally incapable of it. Let me stress that you shouldn't let scruples of any certainty that you will never sleep with David prevent you from living with him: he knows and accepts this possibility.

In the matter of personal traits I can recommend no one more highly. David is more kind and generous than I can be, and I would live with him myself, but he has never asked me to, and I can do him no good.

God help me here. David has an illness which he thinks you can cure, and he may be right. He doesn't want you to stay with him to cure his illness, but because he loves you. I don't know why I want you to stay with him; there is chance enough that you can help him, for me to urge you to try. By "try" I mean nothing more, as far as you're concerned, than sharing an apartment with him, and being yourself. I cannot describe David's illness to you at any greater length here. It is spiritual.

Should you decide against living with David after giving it a try, or even before you come to Salinas, you will always be welcome to stay with me, as we had planned. Think it over and write to me.

Your friend,
Sheeper

P.S. He is willing to drive to Texas to get you.

Jonas, who knew Brian, described him as a Hitler youth raring to burst into the flames of faggotry. Lay this on Sheeper's bit about scruples. Sheeper is such a con, he almost deserves not to live. Just when you think he is being real sincere, he is agreeing with a contrary opinion offered by Jonas. And the bit about David's illness pure soft soap—lubricant jelly perhaps, kindly provided by Sheeper for Brian's ass. Such is Sheeper's love for David. Let me make it clear that David's illness has some foundation in fact. For example, David believes in it. Formerly when you were talking to David you would discover a third party present, whom David was treating with great deference—his illness. Now it flickers in and out of the conversation like a disaffected ghost. Sheeper has no faith in David's illness, David knows it. David's voice no longer believes in his illness, and refuses to be used to discuss it without changing register. Compare Oliver's mad eyeballs when he talks of all the fish he's swallowed.

Since I mention Jonas, let me say something about him. His mama fed him two pints of cream and turned him out. (She closed the apartment and returned to her lover.) His pride makes him pretend to passion (I go out of my head screwing a chick, I spent $20 on the roller coaster, pot really turns me on, *Old and the New* is the greatest flick ever made). Like a good hunter-and-fisher he piously believes the passion will come eventually (it never has). Jonas lives at the source of all magic. His dainty antelope hoofs tap the lino-

leum gently and impatiently as he waits for me to answer
the door. His breath is sour grass, and his glossy skin
emanates a fragrant animal odor which perfumes his clothes.
I nuzzle him and feed him glasses of milk. "Just like my
mama," he says.

To call *The Old and the New* a flick, what disrespect. I'm
gonna take in a flick—meaning *The Old and the New*. To
ask the girl who fixes coffee for the office in the morning
(her face is splashed with milk), "Did you ever see a flick
called *The Old and the New*?"

11

MOTHER

AKBERG'S MOTHER, who neglected him brutally during his childhood, and inflicted hurts which will never heal (she fed him behind the toilet in her barber shop, and placed him in an orphanage at the wish of her lover), spent her last few years repentant. She worked when she was an old lady and sent her son to Europe, to write. She sent him every nickel that she earned, above the cost of her board and room, and she lay dead in her apartment five days before her corpse was discovered. Akberg speaks of her sweetly, and in his work he hides the pain she caused him, he falsifies it even, which proves that he did forgive her and that a mother may earn her redemption. Witches of the world, whiskered (all this in *Macbeth*): note use of the double augmented effect at the twenty-third bar of the theme.

Everything I am or ever hope to be I owe to my angel mother.

Mama you're the only girl I'll ever love. So don't talk to me about marriage and grandchildren, you can't have your cake and eat it. Mama if you had had any conception of the love I had for you, you would not have pinched me under the table (you never pinched me tokenly, but always to hurt

—and the fact that you did this hurt me more than all the pinches, all approximately twenty-five of them, over the fifteen years or so that your hands spent some time each day in the vicinity of my body). The under-table pinches were the worst, because they were hidden and unexpected, and because you violated my body for the sake of some social convention which you felt I had broken—and at least one of which I broke quite innocently. A lady friend of yours (and you had a large number of these single or widowed lady friends, old Lesbian mother, is that why you hurt me so much?) gave me three pairs of socks for my birthday (clothes, is that any kind of gift for a child?). When she left you said they were cheap socks. The next time she called she asked me how I liked them, and I told her they were cheap. You struck me in the face. All right, I grant that you were trying to demonstrate to your lady friend how you dealt with flagrant discourtesy, I grant that by hurting me you hoped to make her feel better, but why, five minutes later, when you passed in front of me, did you have to pinch me so viciously and secretly? You couldn't keep your hands off me. Either you pinched me, or beat me, or you would love me and jack me off.

Mama if you had any conception of the love I had for you, you would not have hit me with belts or straps, which you used to keep on the top shelf of your linen closet, and there would have been a pang of shame mixed with the pride with which you used to open the door of that linen closet and announce to your friends, "I don't send nothing out to the laundry, I do it all myself, the washing and ironing." Shame, for what you said was simply not true. You gave out all the sheets and pillowslips, and since these were the most conspicuous items in the linen closet, it was a mortal deception. Hearing you give your linen closet speech used to make the skin inch on my back. But I forgave you for this, and I would have forgiven you for a moderate amount of corporal punishment, but you went beyond the limit, my flesh still stings.

Mama if you had any conception of the love I had for you, you would not have violated my body with caresses as well as blows. Always you forced responses from me, you asked me every night how I liked the dinner you prepared, and before I had a chance to answer, you told me how good the salad was, or the gefilte fish. How could I give you an honest answer? You fondled my body until I had an erection, and then . . . I lay trembling. You overwhelmed me and never gave me a chance to choose you and kept being too much stimulation. Why were you so untrusting? I think I would still be your lover now—if indeed I am not. You liked me as a young boy, well and good. Think what a morsel I would have been at fifteen.

12

ABOVE THE FRUITED PLAIN

THE BOYS who sit on fire hydrants make eyes at me sometimes just want a chance to put me down. But wait—is
what I'm thinking really true? Is it possible that what they
want is the same as what I want? Street boys come forward
and defend the honor of your intentions.

But I keep thinking that one street boy wants a proposition
and then wants to put me down. At least he wants a proposition, that much is not the product of a diseased imagination.
Every time I pass him he looks at me, no matter how hidden
he is by friends, on the sidewalk, sitting on steps, inside a
luncheonette, playing cards, pennies. Once he pointed me out
to a friend as a character, not sincerely, I noticed from his
forced guffaws.

"We want you to take us for a ride and feel our knees (big
boy ain'cha), tell us about fucking, buy us a milk-shake, jack
us off (orgies in your room come later). Don't fail us, we
count on you, wait for you, mothers hip, want us to be nice
to you, ask us no indiscreet questions. At our age our pricks
hardly go down, like another being occupies them, we let
him have his way, shoot to the roof of the car. So oblige us
already, you want us to crawl on the ground, bluejeans and
briefs at our feet, tee-shirt hanging down open at our bellies

(white or tan, young muscle just forming, skimmed by fat)
or slipping up to our armpits?"

I write the pornography a prim young secretary enjoying
a secret lewd life types at home fast and faultlessly. She gives
a fifth carbon to Piglin, the office boy, as a kind of come-on.
This young lady lives in such cobwebs of neurotic timidity,
she is not aware all she has to do is touch Piglin accidentally
in some office alcove and she will be fucked and finished in a
minute. Even as a child Piglin couldn't keep his hands out of
his pajama bottoms long enough to say prayers. Is it good for
a youth to be so consistently arousable?

Mother and I went down to camp to get good civilian jobs
on an airbase. We were both wearing beards. She said, "You
stay home and I'll get the job. I don't mind shaving off my
beard." To have fought off all her idiocies—thank God I
did—and to fight them through. What would she think of a
Mexican cock—she'd like it—but of me sucking it—in bed
on my knees—for dear life—the hard brown tip—in and out
in and out—in—the pause—held off—now held off—cold
sweat on his ass—squirt squirt squirt squirt—America what
a good boy am I!

Calling all dinge queens and size queens—control your
appetites—it is slightly unpatriotic to stalk spade trade—
better let them make babies. The hope of a land lies wiggling
in the blue black balls you love to cup. What Le Rois swimming in sperm might you swallow? To black we turned
when the snowy Salem spirit was like to freeze our quills—
as to black turns the whole bleached-out land, that will live
thanks to Negroes that never stopped balling. Now smell
their sperm in our work—in these poppies jacked up like
their asses. Try to keep your sucking white a few years
longer. Help the civil rights movement.

Keep in mind what George Washington sucked at Fort du Quesne when his hair was red—a pimply bad-mannered drummer boy from Philadelphia, but so what, this is war. In the middle of the night the Father of Our Country got up to gargle, and thought "Feh! Never again! It makes me feel so creepy." But one look at that drummer lying naked in the dawn's early light, one hand on his chest, the other holding his huge yonge pricke, and that slavering redhead was at it again. The boy crowed softly.

Contrast Piglin's perpetual half hard-on with Washington's short cock resting on his balls like an eye, whose ruffed collar finally unfolded like a a hand organ, but even then not till he had the drummer's cock in his mouth, and even so he was jacking himself off as hard as he could.

I never suck people out. I suck them in. With litachur and phoney pot smoking. Frozen mudras. What de-ontogeny. Sheeper is only sixteen. Imagine de-ontogenizing a fish at sixteen and such a finished product. Blinding.

Why wasn't I born to lipsmacks? Why do I eat standing up, sulking? Having grown a handsome curly brown beard I am laughed at by a little boy who always shouts to his friends when he sees me: "Here comes the bearded lady!" I think of myself as Brahms, surrounded by children. My lip cracks when I smile.

No! I won't write this elegant drivel. Fuck it or flay it I got a hard-on that won't go down. Instead of underwear I wear a jockstrap. A Jewish mama says viping her eyeglasses: "So vat. Maybe he exercises." (I model these good Jewish mamas after my Aunt Ida, who used to give soup with bones they could suck to old Jewish bums. She saved me from thrity whippings in the course of my childhood by placing her short stout body between me and my mother. She was no blood relation.) The only exercise I ever do is putting on a jockstrap in the morning. "God forbid maybe he has a *killa.*" A *killa.* From what, stooping to put my foot through a strap? (Much less than feed bums, my mother held me to believe all strangers filthy *ipso facto,* even Jewish strangers, and now I long to run my fingernail down the seam behind the row of shirt buttons on every man in this movie house. I know I will find no lice or dozing bedbugs. But if I do, if I do O God or Hand which made me—and my fingernails are never too clean and Hawthorne was an asshole—if I do, these insects will burst into gold and red blood, they will be the gold lice crawling in the seams. And I told a friend of mine to put a porcelain filter in his aorta to catch the pallid treponema. Change the filter when it turns silver—the blood flows slow. And silver or blue and gold lice are dashing all over me. I have a precious dharma to transmit. Get back to the grindstone and perk up your ears and cocks.)

I wear the jockstrap because it feels like a hand is holding my crotch all day long, and it leaves my ass naked and soft under my pants. Remind me to jack off with hand lotion. I didn't always know what I kept my ass bare for. I would wake up in a strange bed with something up it and rectal orgasms all over the place, and soon after I would pull up my jockstrap and leave. I was afflicted with the same kind of amnesia during my childhood and adolescence, for I did get myself fucked several times, I know it for sure, but then I didn't wear a jockstrap, only thin cotton shorts, which were taken off completely, except for the first time, when I was nude to begin with—how wonderful Art that I can transform these fancies into memories breaking through an amnesia—the only finger up my ass was the black thumb of the enema—and by the time I had hair on my face I was so ugly and nervous that no one would look at me twice. I was a mosaic of the sexes, a sphinx with a woman's lips on which I used gobs of pomade, a man's thick nose and dry forehead, an old woman's mustache. I developed a flaming red eczema on my cheeks and great patches of dandruff in my hair, which I always kept wetted.

A Moroccan boy is not at all adverse to being screwed, as a rule he likes it better than fucking others while he is young. He learns to fuck by being fucked, and during all the period of hero worship of older boys and men (which we have in America too but with the sex hushed-up) he is regularly being fucked by them and oh! enjoys it more than a woman. He doesn't dream all week that maybe Mohammed will take him to the soccer match but that maybe Mohammed will fuck him again in the stands. He wholly turns himself into a passive pleasure-giving being soul-kissing and making asshole contractions better than any cunt and twisting with passion and sighing voluptuously as your cock goes in deeper and deeper. It is Heaven.

U.S.A. tourists never learn the artful workings of a young Moroccan asshole because the tourists all go to get fucked. Maybe in the nineteenth century American visitors used to keep boys to fuck them, but nowadays they keep them strictly for the size of their meat. So when some American novelist and thirty-year resident of Morocco lets it be known that he is keeping a boy in addition to his wife—like any good Moslem—to add to his glamour—rest assured who is getting what in the ass. Arabs practice a safe sure method of natural birth control which is to fuck their wives in the ass. I demand this technique be added to the birth control manuals now being distributed clandestinely by the City of New York. Let us note in passing that thousands of Moroccans have been trained by U.S. Peace Corps workers to stand still for blow jobs, though oral sex is normally shunned by the fellahin masses.

Think of an American boy minus that goddam axe of fear in his brain to chop off your cock only wanting to give him what his eyes and shy manners want and invite in spite of his brainwashing. Think of him belly down on the bed, his bluejeans pushed down to his ankles. He is one who doesn't wear underwear. The skin of his buttocks is very pale, and he is looking up at you with quiet blue eyes. Without dropping his eyes, he spits into his fingers and wets his own asshole. Please fuck him.

If you have to fuck Americans you will come across ones who think being fucked the floor of abasement, and serve up their ass to get just what they think they deserve. As sometimes Jonas, whom I painted as a gazelle or warm animal, sees himself as a piece of shit and begs me to treat him that way. He snuggles his ass on my belly (last week he was putting down queers). I ask him if he wants me to fuck him. His eyes are shut tight. He says "Yes, please." I oblige. It makes him feel better.

Sex as you like it is an animal right—no mere civil liberty. Defend it with your beak and claws. Defend it and seduce all who don't ball or we'll all be sucked up. And when the copper bosses tell you to fuck Anaconda cunt just roar like McClure and fuck what you want. And when you are told to mope and sleep alone every night a biff in their face with your lion paw asserts your right to animal heat against the cold. Eat shoplifted cupcakes in each other's lairs! Glut till the bestial rhythms you were born to live by appear! Glut to your taste! Cock cunt or face! Animal rights are inalienable.

13

HONEY

THE NEXT DAY, in a stiff chloral hangover (just a headache) I read and live in a pale golden light. That vein in my head poureth blood all over my brains. My love for David is white lace, he's a schmuck, and have opened a vein in my head. The taste of your Judaism like semen depends on what you've been eating. You step over Christianity and let it rage on in ecclesiastical periodicals underneath. Buddhism is the sweet honey of chloral, and I would rather prostrate myself before a sweet golden Buddha than hear W. Lloyd Warner huff and puff. Bugs which alight (tap), pause, and then clatter away. You probably have no idea what I mean by white lace, something silly and light, effeminate and pussy. All your great gods, what would they think of an observation as prosaic as that. Never mind what they would think, each time I open them to be blinded, I find plenty of cribbly prose sentences with bad thoughts like a light little fart. Buddhism can even be the sweet hang of pot. Try to eliminate food altogether. No no, give in, when your mouth is sucked dry by the cube of internal sugar, sip on hot sweet coffee, eat eternal foods, hot thick honey, thin infusions of hay. Underwear lying here and there, that's sweet too, buttered tea. What would you imagine majoun to look like, hipskin? Indeed not, transparent pink and orange cubes of jelly flecked through with shreds of hasheesh, bent and twisted like chromosomes. Old David-love is lacey, loose uncircumcised skin, you can find love in Cairo, or honey in some American's hair. Does anything make a home and family more than a saucepan of hot milk or a glass on a saucer? I can tell you I have never been more mixed up with sweets, and I heft the box of sugar on the kitchen table every time I sit down. Sweets, sweet scratching, criminal longing, are you crying? Sweet longing to be a student of Nostradamus.

A golden stream queen, for your information, is not a Buddhist heresiarch. From the first light golden tap of water on water, to "do whatever you want, that will be our agreement" is a span of twenty years, and sitting in a bathtub to be pissed on is a little bit like fumbling with rubbers. I guess a person has to live rather more aquatically than writing a book would allow, shooting piss from a held cock, sperm and all the rest of it, white discharges and no stiff spots on a handkerchief, because the handkerchiefs are all wet—not to speak of the pages let alone author. And Blank's stomach— we don't divulge the identities of our clientele.

I was healed by the great slime power of Peter's love. If he sees you are sad he will sit on the arm of your chair licking your forehead because it is chapped. "You should use a little baby oil," he will say between licks. I kept him company while he took a bath, and he gave me a puppet show with the mouth of his penis. He twisted and bowed the lips underwater as he spoke all the roles. Then he pulled his foreskin up to signal the end of the performance.

Peter is all golden—all sweet is golden, this pot fact is transcendental, all you kewpies who think sweet is silver open your eyes. Can someone be cellophane?

Vamps and bloodsuckers, bleaches and needling pedestri-

ans. Writing a sentence is scraping a fish. I sew the stanzas up
in these long prose passages, really tiresome rhythms, trying
for the same thing always, to tune the sentence (to screw it
till just before it snaps). And why I take all this time doing
it in face of the fact that certain nameless poets with whom
I have been known to be seen write six lines and give it a
title like "Chunks of Carp" I don't know. You start with a
limestone cock and flute it. All I'm trying to say is I'm a bad
old poet, and good ones ever forgive me, and can't do anything with a foot but boil it. Or bed it in plaster, I can cut a
hunk of plaster like cake. Try to eliminate food altogether.
And having such a hard time with paragraphs, which is getting more and more recedeful. Not to speak of pages, em-
pires, chloral, honey, a blaze of starvation like a month
steeped in the taste of lipstick.

Watch Piglin steal a lipstick from his girlfriend's pocket,
twist it open, bite it off, and chew it down. He kisses her
forcibly. She can feel his cock push against her belly, and his
whole mouth is perfumed with lipstick. His brash turns to
jelly. "Eat me," he pleads, "oh eat out my heat."

14

A CASE OF SOCIOLOGESE

D AVID SAYS, "I wonder how it happens that people with
lower class backgrounds like yourself" pause "or like
me become spoiled." This innocent-sounding remark bears
ramifications that will occupy the memoir for two pages at
least.

To begin with, the common reader ought to have some
understanding of W. Lloyd Warner's theory of social class
in America, that is to say, if the common reader had any
interest in understanding, on a first reading, the full intentions and implications of David's remark. I can't help ex-
pressing the belief that one can go through life very com-
plaisantly, ignorant of Mr. Warner's earth-clattering contri-
bution to sociology, the only penalty being an occasional
blank card when David or some other intellectual deals out
a careful "lower middle class" or "upward mobility." But it's
worth a few blank cards to keep your thoughts about boys
and their boners uncluttered with the eggshells and orange
peels of the social sciences, take it from someone with little
pieces of wet newspaper in the brains.

To understand David at once, it would have also been
necessary for the reader to have formed a very good opinion
of David's scientific intelligence. For when David says "lower
class," he means something very precise. He has in mind a

list of occupations, an annual income, certain types of dwell-
ings, and so on, and he has a fixed statistical weight attached
to each of these ponderables, as we shall call them (because
they pass through David's mind in the form of dark clouds).
The only point I am trying to make is that David does not
place people into social classes casually. Therefore it is of
some interest to know that my background is lower class, in
the exact Warnerian sense, and David's is upper middle class.
I can think of three reasons for David's cheat (for alas it is
a cheat). David (like Jonas) wants to belong to whatever
club the other person belongs to, David doesn't want me to
exploit him or deplete him in any material way (let us skip
the interpretations), and David doesn't want to seem to be a
rich faggot. Nothing makes him deteriorate faster than this
imputation.

Sheeper is only sixteen, imagine a boy writing a memoir
at sixteen and such a finished product.

I think he would like to be a rich faggot, that's the trouble.
He wants to drive a white Jaguar in white swimming trunks,
he wants to wear sunglasses with extravagantly bulging
lenses and thick black frames, he wants to tail an old truck
loaded with sugar beets for five miles, until the young Mexican driver slams on the brakes, and walks over to David,
laughing (the driver is laughing—ambiguous participles, go
mix up someone else's prose). Notice how nonchalantly he
mentions an invitation he has received to spend a weekend
in the country.

I can't let this opportunity go by, of pointing out how
David as a rich faggot would clothe himself in the external
anatomy of the insect world. We invest ourselves with the
wings and angles and eyes of an insect (all this is in *Macbeth*,
look at any costume), and I have more veils to pull from your

eyes, look at the Apollo of Critias or the bronze driver from Delphi, the Parthenon a cell for Athena the Bee, I see the hand of every Ictinus in the head of a grasshopper, Style belongs to the insects.

The artistic tension of the Parthenon lies in its barely perceptible threat to tremble, to liquefy, to become something human and alive. A cockroach is terrible because it has the appearance of an insect (high style), but it strives to be base and human. It is the exact opposite of a high fashion model, or of an interior decorator or copywriter (or novelist) at a cocktail party.

All insects but roaches are born to style (think of a chrysalis), but there is such a thing in a roach as dying in style. This does not mean you begin to tremble, suddenly flop on your back, vibrate a moment, and expire. It means you start running frantically up and down walls, wobbling a bit as one leg and then two become paralyzed, but carrying on nevertheless. It means finally, when running is no longer possible, that you have had the foresight to collect a huge fluff of dust to make you look formidable, and that you stretch open those almost vestigial wings for a pyrotechnical attempt at flight (a flop or two), you land on your back, discharge a plump shiny egg case (save the children), wriggle your legs twice and expire.

I can't let this opportunity go by, without reporting that cockroach wings are fully functional in Pupukea, on the north coast of Oahu, an island as cockroach-ridden, inside and out, as Jonas's apartment—"they don't bother me, they go away when I turn on the light." There the roaches fly around like moths, and God or whoever invented this obnoxious insect has used steel wool on the enamel of its back to matte it, and there they walk perfectly straight and symmetrically, without the ugly stagger of our stateside kind—in fact there they are agricultural roaches, and spit in their faces who say that cockroaches have to live in cities.

I would rather step on a wad of bubble gum in August than hear W. Lloyd Warner huff and puff—and would have spared you all this if David didn't muff a line. Let's give him another chance. David says, "I wonder how it happens that people who were not brought up in the lap of luxury, like you or me, become spoiled." By spoiled David means this about me: I refuse to apply for a job or ask for anything. By spoiled David means this about himself: I refuse to make it with anyone over sixteen (unless he's famous).

15

DAVID SHOT AT

AND NOW MY NERVES, my arteries, everything that branches into filaments in my flesh have been screaming horror for hours. I can't begin to tell you how badly he uses me. He undresses in front of me. He pretends I am a barracks buddy of his (but one cock of my eye sends him scurrying into his underwear). He tries to piss in front of me. He stands before the toilet bowl thinking thoughts like this: "I *am* going to piss now and will not brook a refusal of my bladder neck to cooperate. Silly and effeminate not to be able to urinate in front of your friends like any other careless young boy." I am convinced he is playing me like an instrument, to torment me or bring me to the point of killing him. And I will do it.

What is he trying to crash down on all of our heads? Then once more I forgive him.

When my desperation and desire for his body break against each other at the insane point of hearing every conversation in the tenement no matter how low or knowing from shoeshuffs and the dog howls of every floor exactly which step in the building someone is on in their steep upward climb, at one hour past the time David promised to return (when I had begged him that the previous meeting be our last and he insisted on one more and I agreed, knowing

53

I was agreeing to days more pain and sleeplessness but I love him), all my lonely sorrow folded in on itself, and David's failure whenever it is in his hands to perform a clear swift action to save me or himself (e.g. he is late only when it is emotionally important to be on time) now and always saves me because it is so deliberately and obstinately destructive that I can forgive it—it melts all my self-pity and I turn my attention to him.

I know everything about him. I am the only one who can put a finger in the little velvet pockets of his mind. I know what he will do if he knocks at my door and I am not home. If there is no note on my door he will leave no note, and if there is a note on a scrap of brown paper under the door he will leave a note on a scrap of brown paper under the door, and if the note is in the keyhole he will leave his note there too. I love him for his dumb passivity.

He would barter all my love for one grand entrance to a cocktail party with Professor X. He is a queen, learning their little games while chasing them. And he likes to be quarrelled over, they will do it, he gave me a jubilant account of four queens screaming at a fifth for stealing him from a sixth. David you heart-flower and banjo-throbber—your rubber Frankenstein face. But reader put not down the queens, ah. They celebrate birthdays and make canapés.

David is sick, he is sinister. He is like an animal, which is what sinister means, thinking of his own blood glowing in his flesh. He is a servant only of forces. Power and sex. He counterfeits sentiments, like the wolf in "Little Red Riding Hood." He races in the woods. I wish I could use him. I wish I could give him what he wants. I wish I could part the cheeks of his ass by spreading his thighs and fuck him over his screams of indignation. I wish I could push his head down on my prick, that I wasn't so hung on gentleness and inviolability. I wish I could give him what he wants in his mouth or his ass (watch him choke but suck even harder, that's right, try to suck my whole ass and body into your mouth).

Jonas ejaculated copiously as soon as my pink entered his ass. Venus had entered his ass.

16

THE LETTER FROM MOTHER

MY DEAR SON SHEEPER:
I hope you are well. This is my final letter to you. It seems impossible to believe that I shouldn't remember you on your 56th Thanksgiving. Please read this letter, it is very interesting. Now I shall conceive and confess in the front of God and then to you that I have been the most rottenous, ugliness and impossible mother in the whole world.

Then I have another confession to make. Yes I have possess you, not only as a child, but something more than the most precious gem in the whole world. Before you came into the world, I lost a little boy just like you. When I became pregnant with you, I had only one kidney and I had to be continuedly under the doctor's care, then I began to worry what you would be like. You came to me very hard. I almost lost my own life. Now do you expect me to give you up so easy?

When I called you on Mother's Day eleven years ago was with good intention to ask how you are and if you would like a nice chack for the holidays. You refused and I asked you why. You answered, that I should look inside of me. So I did. Believe me there isn't hardly left anything inside of me, after I went thru six major operations and three minor.

All I have left is, my brains and part of my heart. I am just like an empty shell. What little I had left and what I had to work with and having a little sick boy and a very sick husband like your father was, and that went on for many years. I had to put up a big fight for your father's life and yours too. With my own illnesses, their was nothing for me to do, but to find any kind of a job and go to work, in order to meet the most necessary things in life, a clean home and good food for all of us. I even went to do some house cleaning and wash dishes in order to keep us three together. What kind of life do you think I had? Was that a happy life for a young woman? In my opinion, I made a good honest success for all of us.

I took good care of your father and made him a well man. Then I tried very hard to bring you up as well as I possible could. I let nothing stand in my way to save your health. When I came to see you fifteen years ago, believe me it was with my good thoughts, because I went to see you was that your father and I were very worried over your health.

Sheeper, if you only know what I went thru with your health. No one will every know, except the doctors that took care of you. I guess I was so busy with all these problems that I failed to be a good mother. I did the best way I know how.

While you grew up I saw you are not inclined to mechanical work. You were always very smart and studious, so I tried to encourage you to go ahead with your education, so we could help you as parents should do. We never expected anything in return only once in awhile, a penny post card. If God forbid something would happen to you, we as parents would be the first one to help you and to stand by you. Believe me dear son I mean this from the bottom of my heart.

I want you to remember one thing, blood is thicker and water. No matter what misunderstanding children and parents have, parents always forgive.

We have excepted you the way you came and the way you are even if you would have been born God forbid a cripple with many defects, but thanks God that you were born with feet to walk, hands to work, eyes to see, smart brains to use them and a mouth to talk. This also was a part of my insides.

Another event I made, we established a little business for ourself so your father wouldn't have to go look for a job each time. We went in this little business without any knowledge or experience, but we learned the hard way. Now thank God we are making a living in a hard way, but it is a satisfaction to know that your father doesn't have to go around in the whole city to look for a job. This was also the brains in my insides.

There is still a little matter to explain. When your friend came over and took me to his home to meet his family, you and he went in the other room, so his wife was telling me how very sorry she feels for you. I asked her why, so she told me that you hardly have any money or any clothes. This alone nearly killed me. I simply could not believe it that my son could go around like this and not give his parents the satisfaction to ask for help when you were so broke.

Sheeper, why didn't you ask us to help you? Did we ever refuse you anything in your life? Then another ugly remark came from your close friend that you envied him because he didn't have any parents. There is one way out, to kill us off. We never hated you, no matter how much heart ache you gave us. I guess your father and I had our difficulties in life, but each one of us tried to do the best we knew how for you.

We never made you leave home, but you left on your own account.

Then the night before I left San Francisco and your friend came in, and you left me alone and he brought a bottle of liquor and also helped himself to the Frigidaire and made himself high balls and dranked and I was sitting and crying thinking what a fine student I got. He kept on drinking and talking and telling me that you did something that I will never know.

What makes all your friends feel so sorry for you? This is my full confession to you, what is inside of me.

You really give us a bad time but we shall always love you because you are my son. I wish you could find a way how to get along with your parents. Life could be so much more pleasant if you would turn a little to us. As a mother I know what kind of a child she has, but you did not give me a chance to help you, not only with money, but you needed understanding and care. You pushed me out of your way. Turn back. There is some hope for you. I cried, and I also looked for some answer and help. No one to talk to and that was the end of my trip to San Francisco. So you see my dear, I knew and felt what my son was doing with himself and I except you the way you are.

There is many men like you, they make the best of their lives and they are happy. Sheeper dear, you still so young, there is hopes for you, why did you have to make your life so bitter? You are against us & against the whole family. Why is it coming to them and to us.? Why do you take it out on us. Why?

Do you think it was our fault? that you were born that way God knows the truth that it isn't, a lot of children are born freaks, yet they keep on living. Why?

Please forgive me if I said something that you don't like, you know deep in your heart that I don't mean it. I am only a human & how much can one take. You don't have to wait ten or fifteen years for an answer. Should I remind you of the fifth commandment or did you forget it at all. Parents always tell their children what to do. As God is my witness I try to explain you the best way I know how. Dont forget that I didn't go to Grammar School to learn how to write English. I am proud of myself that I learned the hard way. I know I make many mistaks, but when I write to people they understand me. So you see my dear that I have for so many things to be thankful.

My dear son why don't you grow up and come to your senses. You remind me when you were a little boy, you said the same words when you got mad at me or at the teacher. I don't want to see you or talk to you.

We did the best we know how and with what little we had.

We dreamd and we hoped when you grow up to be a man that you will give us a little pleasure to let us hear from you once in awhile, that we wouldn't have to look for you all over the world, and spend so much money for telephone calls. I am plenty disgusted with you. As a Son you are a complete failure, as a man I don't know. We have tried to do the best for you but the best wosn't good onought for you.

You can't hold conversations by writing letters, may I ask you one little favor to call us up on the telephone to hear your voice. Please reverse the charges.

Please answer this letter and I send you a nice chack for a gift. I hope you will answer this letter, it is very *importen.*

I hope you will understand why it is so importen for you to answer this letter. And I would like to have your home address so the mail could come direct to you.

I took the privilege to send you a few cookie. Please except it. This was the first time that I was able to bake in a long time, as I fell and injured both hands. My left hand left me with a blood clot and my right hand broke a bone above my fingers. I am in a cast since October 9th. The two fingers in my right hand, the doctor left out, so I manage trop you a line. Please believe us what we did we meant the best for you but things don't work out that way. This world is big and nature is beautiful. Every person must find away how to live in it. We all have disappointments and laughs too, in life most in life is disappointments.

Hope some day that you will meet a nice girl and settle down and get married and have a little home of your own. Married life is not so bad. It has their advantages and disadvantages when you grow older you have one another.

This is something that I don't know, if you are married to some one that you are ashamed of. Dont be ashamed it happens everyday in life. The least you could do is to let us know.

Have you ever stop thinking why your father wants to know your address? Don't you realize that he will be pretty near 90 years old. It is later than you think. I can wait. I will be 77 years old. It is quite a different in our ages. I also have more patience than your father. But we are old and no more dreams for us.

Each time I make up my mind, that I wouldn't write to you, but how can a mother forget a son like you. You know deep in your little heart we always trusted you since you were a little boy I talked to you as you were a big man. I know that you don't love your parents, but we love you. You still our blood in flash. I shall always forgive you, because I am a mother and you are my son.

We know one thing the mail don't come back. I called

you several times, but the answer is they don't know where you are and you left no forwarding address. Who is lying and where is my mail going to? So you see dear why we don't send anything. How can we send you a gift or chack? Your father says he is still waiting for your address, as we would like to send you some underwear and shirts and socks. We are getting them strictly wholesale. Kindly send us the sizes you want and the sleeve lengths. Is there any linens, sheets, towels and pillow cases you can use. Is there any medicines that you need, send us the prescriptions and we will get them at cost. We also manage to save enought money to send you nice chack, a dollar for every month in the year. I know my dear that one can always use extra cash, even if you don't need it, it is nice to have it in reserve. We don't need so much and we will try to help you as much as we can. I am your mother and I shall always stand by you, you don't have to pay me back and you don't owe me anything, unless you will become a very rich man, then you may send me a little gift if you want to.

Please believe me my dear that this comes from the bottom of my heart.

There isn't one day or one moment or whatever I do that I always think of you. Please write and let me know your address and I shall mail you the chack. I promise that your father wouldn't know, I have to keep many things away from him he is getting older and he is not responsible for so many things that he is doing. The patience I had with him and with you, made me a better woman and I larned to understand many people.

Please believe me that I love you more than ever, you are my blood and flash and you my only son that I ever had.

Why do you hurt me so much, by not writing to us? At lease you have parents, I wasn't so lucky.

One more thing I would like to ask you if you would like to come back to New York, believe me you could find planty of work here its nice to come home where you was born. Your nice clean room and soft bed is still waiting for you.

You think that I would write such a letter with such a clear explanation. From now on it is up to you. God is my witness, that as a mother, I certainly have offered you the best of my understanding, and I am sure that some day soon you will never be happy until you will for fill my sincere wishes, and that comes from the bottom of my heart. With love from a mother that will never forgets her son God Blass you x x x x x

      Love
        Mother

17

MATERNAL CARE
EXHIBITED BY FEMALE EARWIG

18

THINGS START MOVING

OBJECTS ON THE FLOOR take on a rocking motion, a wad of dust, a dead roach, a pair of shoes. As I keep watching, the roach and wad of dust begin squirming. A shoe moves two inches.

Does marijuana kill pain? I pinch a bit of loose skin on the back of my hand and feel nothing. Apparently it does. One should be careful not to injure his body, pain the protector has been banished. Moments later I feel a long, sharp sting on the back of my hand. Two things come to me, as if they were two horns of the same realization. How pot intensifies any stimulus. How pot pulls out time like a long strand of tar or taffy-candy.

A particular word in the upper third of the page begins to scintillate, a yellow fluster of stars surrounded by a radiant dark violet field. A numb graininess falls into my arms, my feet, up into my head. A great half whirl, a child's hollow metal top, slashing lines. The memory of walking upstairs in a previous pot high. The yipe of a dog and I was penetrated by a silver fencing sword.

My mind is swiftly passing through long canals of thought lock by lock. A marvelous realization occurs to me, and I am applauded by an audience of mental hands. My healthy predatory mind stalks through five planets looking for food

65

before it returns to this page and to the idea that it had something more to say. My mind forces my hand to write about thoughts which are still being formed by the very energy my mind is using to force the hand. (In the middle of writing the previous sentence I completely forgot the way I had cast it, and so was unable to finish it, while at the same time I had no trouble retaining the thought which I could not express. I finished the sentence and added this note later.) I try to re-read the previous sentence, going backwards carefully, word by word, but I give it up. My mind has invaded my hand physically, forced itself down into my fingers. It wants to express itself directly, without the medium of hand or fingers, it wants to *be* its expression. Meanwhile the hand goes on writing, my eyes travel up and down my forearm, all encyclopedias open themselves to three-dimensional photographs of American fields and mountains. It is clear that I am being invited to walk into the photographs, but the landscapes are parched and brown. My mouth is dry. Roy is in the kitchen cutting onions on a wooden table, the knock of knife on wood keeps time to a Rollins solo. (It takes me five minutes to write the words knock and knife, which are mixed up in my mind. Finally I am able to separate them and painfully spell out one and then the other.) The music stops. My mind feels brought down and depressed, withdraws itself from my hand, which stops writing. Shadow of a hand dawdling with a pen. Insects flash out into the light from the black shadow thrown by a milk carton. Insects appear on the floor, chase back and forth in short zigzags, vanish when I discover my own head is swaying back and forth. Roy is in the kitchen making noises which I cannot identify.

19

STYLE

THERE ARE TIMES I am incapable of carrying one idea through two sentences, and I am surrounded by a flock of independent thoughts, like birds in a private aviary, some sentenced, some half-sentenced, sometimes words without thoughts—and I am tempted to catch them and write them as they hop from one side of my mind to the other—or there are times when I see these thoughts in a more collected frame of mind (small birds asleep on their perches) and I am tempted to lay them out in order like cigarette papers when several joints are being rolled at once, like gummed leaves, gummed because they must be capable of being stuck to one another in some way, they are all from the same Mind.

Here Oriental Piglins were to pelt eccentric Hakuin with baby octopi. Here Pericles was to be persecuted with the arrest of his architects. Here Allen was to be begged not to let food fall on this page, grains of tobacco, even in the oldest books dusty patches of black and white back at the fold blooms of mold ashes from the pipe of a man settled down to read away an evening. Here Sheeper was to pose in vain for his portrait as a leaf gum artist. Here Sheeper was to spare you a digression on his cock. (He wrote one and dumped it. It was to go right here—the principle being

not to let any hole parenthetical or otherwise slip by without
stuffing it. O learn from the Arabs!) Here Allen was to yap
and yell at you to cut out all your conceits. O let me keep
one page of preteritions—as Heliogabalus pled before the
whole Roman army to be left just a single queer lover.

Here Franco, standing in his bathroom, was to shave the
black hairs from his fingers. Here David, standing naked in
the stall shower of his family's master bedroom, was to have
a fourth go at his wrists, and the last pair of scars not yet
blanched. In my dreams his hands come down on me like
parachutes. Here Piglin, having come out too pretty, was
to suffer a little-finger pile or chronic ass-itch, or a sprink-
ling of big warts on his hands. Piglin and David have the
same complexion, and there is a pig-sticking quality to the
fog of suicide which surrounds David.

Professor X complains I have no loyalty to my characters
and neglect to tell what finally happens to them all. But
this is an English ship on the Spanish main, my dear Professor, a gold-hound with a very short gangplank.

Professor X complains that sex as I describe it is all itches,
that I don't trust any human emotion enough to carry it
beneath the skin. But I do trust the news before 1910, as-
signing such reportorial boners as the great Throne Room
griffon hatching eggs (when the point was the first chiaros-
curo in Western art) to the pedantical drone of Sir Arthur
Evans. And I trust all early advertisements and directions,
for example for Fitting Eyeglasses, printed on the inside of
a box cover along about 1868 or 1869. As far as human
emotions go, I fabricate them like a boxful of old-fashioned
eyeglasses—no matter how deep in the box you go the emotion is like a pair of spectacles, with gold wire frames at
that, or a pince-nez. I see a farmer's wife with just such a
pair of spectacles, sticking a pig. In the farmhouse a light
wind is blowing thin flowered curtains.

Professor X complains that my book is about style and that's all it's about. He is right. All you reading rate controller addicts and skimmers, all you commuters who want some *meat* in a novel, leave mine alone. (Fuck the rhetoric, he is wrong. This book is about a mental shift.) But the style of this memoir is the style of my life as I lived it, the style of my skin disease. I do not attempt to represent the style of my life by the style of the writing, the styles are the same, they are identical. I am indifferent to whether I have intercourse with words or feelings or people, the One Style encrusts and encompasses them all. And, making allowances for goodness and badness, it is the same *type* of style which insects manifest and which fashion designers employ. Take any male fashion designer who loves to be fucked in the ass, or any queer copywriter or advertising artist. The style of their work, in all its corruption, is the same as the style of this memoir. Is it Good? Who knows. I have to employ it until the itch stops.

Professor X complains that my style too obtrudes and names ten writers who have rubbed out their own. But for them the margins of a page are a window frame. They are window cleaners who want to show you life, they wash away the lines of print. I hate writers who put their tongue to this use. "It is the perfection of art to conceal art" makes me shudder. I want the printed line to intrude constantly, I want the reader's focus to shift continually, I want each image broken and complemented by a word or sound and fixed by the spike of style the way a cucumber is spoiled and preserved by pickling or a snapshot held on the wall by a tenpenny nail. And besides, I want to express no thought which is not involuted, no idea which is not intertwined like garlands with literal print on the literal page. Everything is itch and scratch, skin, surface, and advertising copy. Everything is sensation, there is no tenderness here, there are mirrors.

You want a telescope? Shoeblack on the rim. For, you
buy a parrot on the U.S. black market (come down with
psittacosis two weeks later), bring it home, pluck it screaming and squawking ("What you doing to that goddam bird,
I'll call the police, sex maniac, go pull out your own feathers"—how the fuck she can hear the bird above her soap
operas blasting all day long)—that's what writing a sentence
is, and all you fans of Henry James, prose bungler and poly-
syllabizer, open your eyes. Here everything shimmers, shatters, shivers, or gleams falsely, unattainably, like gold. Or
everything is the SWEET dull first pale break of gold (Piglin crushes his wedding band).

I am a light wind blowing thin flowered curtains, and
boys where they want to go, while prose is a tiny candle
flame flickering, and the wind makes a curtain bottom
creep on the sill like a spider.

Franco I worship your style, I am a Fascist. The death
of the Jews, the wraiths of Lidice or Alcubierre, the Plaza de
Catalunya, rats apanic at each other, your Spanish Moroc-
cans, *maricones,* brown soldiers with a bundle of rods—
Franco your mausoleum, your Dali, the black church of
Spain, valley of the fallen, Infanta, the kiss of hemophilia.
Franco you black flower, I want your hand in soft places
(Whitman, old man, turn in your sleep). The pinch of steel
kisses. Franco you worship Death and know Death and
marble and black Catholic cities. Franco, generalissimo,
stab me (Ethiopian), Baudelaire of Spanish rumbling, black
Iberia, the glacier of Pericles, thin blue flower. Back to cre-
matory smoke. Pirate, your flat sad arrogant face, sweet
hands. The lace and lisp of the Infanta are in your face,
Franco. Franco, Hadrian, the death you spread over Spain
like wildflowers.

Part Two

20

BELLY BEAT

ALLEN IS compulsively poetical. I drop in with Roy's Wife, who has been trying to take her husband's place (he is back in jail). She wears his clothes and smokes his pot. Tonight she is on goofballs. She decides to write a letter to Roy. She is in the next room, writing and sobbing. She says, "Man what's the word for mess and flesh in the family, you know man, mess and flesh." Allen stops his conversation with me to call out: "That's it! Mess and flesh."

For Allen claims that what Genius forces the hand to say should never be changed or thought over. Yet his mind always dredging, always digging and plowing up the surface makes me nervous. And here we sit like two outmoded adding machines, crocheting a passage in Marrows' great novel from twelve different manuscript versions. We are very offhand about suggesting the order of images—as if to each of us writing wasn't a paralyzing, devious art. And we each knew and feared the secret of the other, which is Power lashed to the page with Art. Art is brains in the sense of permutations explored systematically, the right complications salted in will be *Genius.* Genius is the scales and choosing. For anything can be wove into lace, the clap of a hand, a man shaving his face after he comes home from work rather than before, shaving away the fine young hairs, palping his face as he shaves it smooth as a penis, he is getting ready for sex tonight. If he doesn't stop shaving, he will be late. His razor yearns to warn him by flying from his hand with a soft clap of wings like a bat. But it is a safety razor, designed to stay frozen with fear of giving up its object nature.

Allen thinks I'm peculiar—a mosaic of the sexes. Well he should talk. Am I always cooking soup bones? Am I always carrying a shopping bag, worrying because a handle tore off? And in the shopping bag bottles? Do I suck the marrow from bones?

Allen tells me my breath smells. "I noticed it before. I had the same trouble and went to a good dentist in Oakland, he gave me gingival treatments, a friend of the family, in fact a distant relative, it's worth the trip. Let me see, here's a card, call him and make an appointment." If you don't have an Allen handy try a smaller screwdriver.

Allen Aristocrat looks to be visited. But Allen Fair Fifty looks to pay back the visits you make. The two Allens merge to visit you for a definite business reason. When Allen invites me over, my body automatically winces. I am allergic to cats, cat powder fills his apartment. My brain aches, my nasal passages close, my eyes weep, my skin erupts. He knows this, wants me to visit him anyway, and I do. We kiss on the pretext of arriving and departing. When he leaves town he kisses much longer kindling the flames.

When Allen quotes Shelley he sets me afire. Later in bed with the book on my belly I drop off to sleep.

Did you ever see a Jewish sadhu camp? Tickle his belly and make him say:

Auntie!
Aunt Solomon!
She loves to be fucked!
Her asshole sends out shocks of musk!

Allen says, "I'd like to be a queen, but I got too much hair on my belly." Somehow that's a very silly remark, and makes me think of a female ape with a little bit of ribbon at the slope-tip of her head—or a piece of Neanderthal trade with a Cro-Magnon pussy. I walked through his pad littered with squeezed-out K-Y tubes which dogged me like a pack of cubs with little tin barks: "Fuck Allen! Fuck Allen!" I saw him beckon with a nervous female sneer— the smell of rubber pussy in the air—my belly curling. Well I say ho hum, leave him mystique, who have shot Amos into art, now I am too asleep, brush the fly away, black velvet belly, glassine wings, a web of black lines on them. But it was only a crossing with another hair as I happened to look at my leg.

21

ETHER

I THROW ALL my knowledge into limbo, so that nothing I know will contradict what Allen tells me. I believe and marvel at everything he says. I follow him around, transfixed. Streets pass, I see only his face.

Allen's epiphany on collating the Olympia *Naked Lunch* with our manuscript: With the end of the novel Burroughs passes from the world of nothing (no glot) into the empty door frame of the honey-Buddha, whose agent Lee has always been. Followed by a big ether high.

(Three boys holding small wads of cotton are lying or sitting on a small divan. One of them, ALLEN, *holds a small can marked with a red skull and crossbones; his index finger covers an opening at the top of the can's short thin neck. From time to time he moistens his wad of cotton by inverting the can over it, then he holds the wad to his nose, at the same time passing the can to* PETER *and* SHEEPER, *who do likewise, and return it.)*

PETER: Allen is always giving lectures. Yeah, he talks for two hours and then he don't know where he is or what he said, so he gets embarrassed, so he continues for another two hours. (ALLEN *listens with a dutiful set smile, but he is pained and anxious, imagining that in this naked outburst*

PETER *will reveal secret negative observations.*) He gabbles on and on and it always comes out the same lecture—all about natural prosody and the variable foot and the long line of Whitman. . . . (PETER *senses that* ALLEN's *feelings are being hurt.*) But the more he talks the more new discoveries he makes, and also he says a lot of new poetry when he gets to talking excited like that—

SHEEPER (*laughing*): You sound just like Roy when he's stoned. He starts a put-down, but he's too nice or compassionate to carry it through, so he changes it mid-stream to a compliment. When I showed him a passage I had just worked on he said, "Kerouac and Burroughs . . . and you and me are the best prose writers in this whole country."

PETER (*after a moment*): All right, why is everybody looking at me, why don't you say what you're thinking Sheeper, you're the one who had to listen to Allen's big lecture on Burroughs, and I was just taking your part. . . .

ALLEN: Yeah, what did you think of it? Bullshit probably.

SHEEPER (*after a moment of cocked-head thought,* ALLEN *and* PETER *waiting for an answer*): Well I can tell you what I was thinking while you were talking, is that what you want to know?

ALLEN (*eagerly*): Yes.

SHEEPER: Well the first thing I was thinking—it's the same thing I think whenever you get all involved and start explaining something to me—at those times somehow I always think—how much I love you.

ALLEN (*kindly and yet sincerely*): We love you too Sheeper, very much.

SHEEPER (*not to be outdone*): Allen if you only knew how much I love you! (*Carried away by sincerity.*) Allen I just adore you.

PETER: I knew all the time that you two intellectuals wanted to make it. Well I'll just go into the other room. . . .

SHEEPER: Peter I love you too. And it's a big strain loving you both, because I get all mixed up, and pulled in opposite ways, and torn up between you. Loving one person is hard enough.

ALLEN: Let's take him to bed with us.

PETER: Yeah! I got a little hard-on. (*He pulls his cock out from his fly.*) Shall I take off my pants? (ALLEN *nods briskly.*) O.K. (*He starts to unfasten his belt, pauses, grasps his cock with the fingertips of both hands and looks at it.*) Maybe I better wash my cock.

ALLEN: You don't have to wash your cock, Peter.

PETER: O.K. (*He continues to unfasten his belt.*)

SHEEPER: Wait! My God! If—if Peter is going to take off his pants, I'm going to need more ether. (ALLEN *hands the can to* SHEEPER, *who moistens his cotton and snuffs it, handing the can back to* ALLEN. PETER *has stopped undressing and waits for a go-ahead signal from* ALLEN *or* SHEEPER.)

ALLEN (*to* SHEEPER, *nervously, and obviously re-structuring the situation*): Which of us do you want to make it with most?

SHEEPER (*after a long pause*): I . . . I can't decide.

ALLEN: I'm willing to make it with you, but I don't really want to, what I mean is, I don't really want to fuck you, but it's all right for you to fuck me.

SHEEPER: Fine! (*Rests his head on* ALLEN's *stomach.*)

PETER: You two are so finical.

ALLEN (*suddenly*): I don't want to be loved! (*He pushes* SHEEPER's *head up and stands. He paces anxiously.*)

SHEEPER (*philosophically*): I always fuck up in the lacework. Leave it to me, frail as I am, to storm through all the big principles and policy hang-ups, cylinders whirling on

the Midway, when you pull up the courage to go through
them they give you gentle loving bumps being all canvas
and watch springs—so I make all the right big decisions,
for which I don't care a bit, and when it comes to fine shad-
ings and fragile details, which absorb me, I blunder. My
Hell is so *natural*. My long perfectly co-ordinated fingers
suddenly trip over each other, bruise petals and tear the bat
wing. I'm dead tired of it. If I can't love anyone finely, on
the grass by a tinkling Elysian brook, without rolling over
into a cowpad, then fuck directing my love to flower. Allen
I take back what I said. I certainly don't love you, it's not
cool for me.

ALLEN: What difference does it make how cool it is, my
God what difference does that make? (*Afraid that* SHEEPER
will interpret this question as an encouragement, ALLEN
turns both hands down in front of him.) I don't want to be
loved.

SHEEPER: But you accept Peter's love, how come you
can't accept mine?

ALLEN: I don't accept Peter's love. How do you think I
hold him? (*Pause.*) I don't want to be loved. I don't need
your love. I already have all I want.

SHEEPER (*mischievously, putting an arm around* PETER):
Then why don't you give Peter up? (ALLEN *screws up his
face.*)

ALLEN: All I know is I don't want your love and I put
you down for it.

SHEEPER (*sadly*): You wouldn't put me down if you
knew me better, if you knew how few people I love.

ALLEN: You wouldn't *feel* put-down if you knew *me*
better.

I walked home in a dark, fuzzy blue dawn—Allen drunk-
love—Allen lacklove—the conk of thunder on thunder—

genesis of Poetry—Allen's spell over me broken—love of me, fear of me—his epiphany: the nothing of all the lust and frenzy of *Naked Lunch* (conk) the empty nothing at the end—irony ain't the pitch, the number to play is 00— split-level Universe—I had improved my condition (I knew where and how close I stood) and permanently made it worse (the wall was up now)—this flash of internal light, my inner finger pointing silently at myself—in the early morning fog, the breath of ether in my mouth

22

A PILL MERCHANT

Riggsy comes on as a Cuban patriot and he showed up one night with a nicely framed Fidel Castro poster which he purportedly just brought back from Cuba. I admired it. He hesitated a moment and gave it to me, as a spontaneous act of generosity, as if he hadn't brought it to barter for something else. A little while later he asked if he could stay with me over the weekend ("This guy is letting me use his pad, but he won't be out till Monday"). I balanced the poster in my mind against three days of being dragged with Riggsy and finally told him he could stay until such time as he bugged me and then he would have to leave. So he took off his boots and lay down on the bed, and in a little while I lay down beside him.

Sex—with men anyway—is a world in which Riggsy operates but refuses to recognize. He asks if he can stay overnight ("Me and the old lady are having a hassle"). In bed if I move just barely to touch him, he will whisper "Go down on me man, please? Aw come on." He says this urgently and automatically, as if to circumvent any show of love or tenderness. I may hold back, and then he takes hold of my head and tries to push it down along his chest. I get very bugged with him for this. I don't mind he is scared and comes on tough like trade, but it hurts my pride to be treated like a cocksucker, and I push his hands away and move to the other side of the bed. Then I feel guilty and relent. Besides his skin is smooth and now I long to kiss his chest and stroke his arms. But he will not love my body, he cannot bring himself to, except at the height of passion, just before orgasm, when he will go down on me and deep—try to swallow my whole body cock first while he masturbates himself furiously. And after all his butch come-on he quite collapses as he comes, whispering "Forgive me! Forgive me!"

He never alludes to these episodes afterwards, and I will tease him for his shame and shyness by saying in front of others, "Last night in bed when you kept pushing my head down, why did you keep doing that?" And he says "What?" with an expression which rapidly dissolves from "You must have been dreaming" to "I must have been dreaming about my chick."

The time he came over with the poster I made it with him and kicked him out in two hours. Nevertheless he left the poster behind, and I gave it a great deal of thought. Usually he "borrows" something just before he leaves—a clean shirt or pair of socks, a dollar, pen or pair of sunglasses, and this was the first time in our long friendship that I ever had more property when he left than before he came. I thought maybe he was loosening up.

About two weeks later he stopped in with a fat older man. "Sheeper, I want you to meet Solomon Horseback, he's very cool." I led them to chairs, and just as soon as they were seated Riggsy said "You want to get high man?" He was holding a joint lengthwise between his thumb and forefinger. I reflected for a moment, said "Hmm. O.K.," took the joint, and let Riggsy light it for me. I inhaled and offered it back to him. He said, "No man, I already had plenty before we came

over." What? Riggsy refuse pot? I've seen him wake from a
sound sleep at the smell of "boo" as he calls it drifting in
from another room. I offer the joint to Sol Horseback, who
says "No man, I'm stoned, that's for you." It has been my
experience that anybody who offers you a joint and then
doesn't join in is getting you high for a definite business
reason.

Anyway the pot was very good, and a bit later I hear
Riggsy say "deathadrine" and Sol correct him, and when I
look up Sol is saying "Pills? Pills you say man?" and he
starts pulling out phials of pills from every pocket. "I'm a
chemist man, what'll you have? Methedrine?" Sol turned to
me. "Here Sheeper, I'm going to give you a couple of methedrine. Man meth will make you go up to the angels—don't
put 'em away, take 'em now. And here is let me see two
mortalin, and you can have a goofball, nembutal, that'll
relax you, and these here pills will put you right to sleep.
And I'm going to leave another set for your roommate." (I
can hear Riggsy telling him "I know a couple of fags who
might buy . . .") He asked me how I liked the pot and I
nodded. "Well I just have a little bit," he said, "but I'll give
you some." All the time he was laying pot and pills on me
I kept feeling (and squelching) "but please let me at least
pay you something for these." He was a salesman conning
me into buying something I had no need of, and each pill he
gave me was carefully meted out—so many free samples for
this apartment and no more. He said that if I wanted any of
the pot, he had a good contact and could get me "an O.Z. or
even half an L.B." What phony argot I thought. There was
a long silence and I sensed Riggsy his agent watching me. "I
would like to buy some from you," I said, "but I have no
bread right now. When I get some, can I reach you through

Riggsy?" "Sure, sure man," he said, looking hard at Riggsy, who took the cue and said dully, "I give you my new address, didn't I?" Sol had to prompt him with the street number. I led the two of them to the door.

When his friend had gone through the door, Riggsy took me aside and asked if I could lend him enough for a pack of cigarettes. "But I have no bread right now," I repeated. "Oh yeah that's right," he said. His eye caught the Fidel Castro poster now on my wall. "Say could I borrow that to have it photographed? I should have brought back two." "Take it," I sighed. He invited me to a party on Friday that I knew would never take place, and with a military handshake, he left with the poster.

Homosexuals of the world! Stand up for your rights! Refuse to let your head be shoved down someone's chest and belly without further ado, but demand to be loved up! Whoever lets you suck their cock as a concession, refuse to touch them! Unless of course you are willing to sacrifice this battle for a larger victory in mind—like hooking this guy on blow jobs—he is very silent and never says anything and you know exactly how hot he is and when to move your mouth onto his prick and he falls in love with you and goes down on you—he wiggles right down on that bed, honey, and starts lapping like a big hungry puppy, and swallows the load with a scared boyish gulp, but he liked it and now he is busy rimming your cock slit with the tip of his tongue—I remember a dike telling me about a fashion model she used to live with, "She went down on me plenty of times, I wouldn't have it any other way"—and you both live in bliss, two creaky old men with white hair and smooth faces sucking each other off till death do you part—and even then you pull away the shroud with shaking hand to plant a tender

farewell kiss on his shrunk cold dick while a hidden stage-
hand shakes thunder from a sheet of steel and down in the
orchestra three final booms from the kettledrum. This is
life! These dreams are life! But don't read them to your
mother or she will jealously fix you with a razor.

23

ROY'S WIFE

I PULL OPEN the Drawer of a Thousand Objects, and we pick up one thing after another, talking and marvelling. I am holding a short orange candle with both ends melted over round and smooth. I have had it for years. Roy's Wife waits for an explanation. "It must be a candle I keep in case the fuse blows out." She bends over my fingers studying the object with all the care I have infused in her for months. "Where's the wick?" she says. "Probably melted over," I reply.

My hands have their own memory and sense of the past. Thumb and forefinger remember pinching a wick at one end of a hand-softened candle and tearing it out. Other fingers join in the memory of smoothing over a long wax scar. I command my hands to reveal their old purpose but they refuse.

I definitely want the candle I am now holding to have a wick I can show Roy's Wife. I scrape a little wax off one end with my thumbnail. No wick appears, and I scrape off more wax. I feel compelled to seem objectively interested in discovering the nature of this object. Roy's Wife senses my embarrassment and offers, "It might be a crayon." I take a sheet of paper and make a long mark down it with the candle. The mark is nearly uncolored. I am silent but she will not release me from the investigation—perhaps to punish my dishonesty—and says, "So what is it?"

"I think it's a candle," I reply, breaking off larger and larger chunks of wax in neurotic quest of the wick. I break the candle in half. There is no wick. I say weakly, "I always thought it was a candle." My hands are cold and filled with broken wax. At last she picks up a small jar of stramony seeds and turns it slowly in her fingers.

24

ROY'S WIFE

ROY'S WIFE and I are listening to records. She pulls a joint from her left ear and lights it. She gives it to me. After passing it back and forth a few times I notice how attractive she is. I want to compare notes with her on being fucked.

SHEEPER: Have you ever run across the type who apologize when they come off? (ROY'S WIFE *nods smiling.*) What are they apologizing for?

ROY'S WIFE: Well I always thought for making babies, but if they apologize to you too I guess not.

SHEEPER: We have to find out if the same man who apologizes to you will apologize to me. We need an Experimental Design, my dear. Why don't you introduce me to more of your boyfriends?

ROY'S WIFE: Why don't you make it with Roy?

SHEEPER: He's in jail.

ROY'S WIFE: You didn't make it with him when he was free.

SHEEPER: He didn't have a hormone left to grow whiskers, much less have an episode with an attractive young sheep.

ROY'S WIFE: He made it with other *women.*

SHEEPER: He finger-fucked them.

88

ROY'S WIFE: He could have stuck his thumb up your ass. Shut up and listen to the music already. Here I give you this pot and you won't even fuck me, but you worm out of it by pleading sisterhood. That's bullshit baby, bullshit. If you don't want to fuck me why did you bring up the subject of sex in the first place. Now you've got me aroused. I ought to pull your prick right out and fuck myself with it. No I won't, I'll think of Roy fucking me, or the Mexican, shut up already and let me dream.

SHEEPER (*seriously*): Did you ever fuck Roy, I mean want to, like with a dildo?

Roy's Wife starts to answer and pouts. Sheeper beams. They listen to a solo of Ray Charles silently.

25

ENTER ROY; TO HIM, WIFE

ROY'S TWO GREAT LOVES were jail and his Wife (which is why she is alone so much), and once I got so mad at him for abandoning her again—not to speak of how hard Allen and I had worked to spring him the time before—I adopted her myself and vowed besides never to write to him in jail or speak to him either. But when he got out he won her back with promises, and I forgave him and speak to him whenever he and his Wife are in town (wearing dark glasses).

Roy's Wife is prow-like and princely independent, and has yoked her nature to Roy's out of love. She says, "I'll go wherever you go, Roy." She tenderly follows all the wanderings and unbelievably erratic patterns of his life, without losing a step. For example, Roy lives entirely by touching his many friends for small sums, and his Wife has scuttled her pride to do so in his stead. And whenever he gets busted she starts wearing his clothes and making his rounds and even picks up on the chicks he has eyes for.

As for that constant handout pressure I found so annoying —I see it now as a call to virtue. For they are always asking: what is more precious to you, a dollar or us? And indeed they are precious and priceless, and if I were to acknowledge this openly and act accordingly, I would be reduced to beggary like them.

I love Roy's Wife because she acts in my favor. She tells David to call me (he demurs). Shine her. God turn her on. Make her razzling dazzling.

Another time Roy was busted, and she didn't even wait to hear charges. She said, "Fuck the Penelope bit, I have broken the coop." So she flew down to Mexico, got a new boyfriend, a pimp I think, and eked out her living as well as she could. A year later I wrote her that Roy was due for parole. She never answered my letter, with good reason.

She is back! The Prince of Wars! Suddenly red, white, and blue! Her hair is dyed black. It is blue and japanned. She hath lain with many men. She hath knocked and I answered not, but I sneezed, and she knew I was listening, and called my name. Her buss is light and so quick it has to be true—a bestowal and not a demand—unlike many chicks I know who transform a hello or goodbye kiss into a long drawn out sticky fuck. O.K. they want you to be their lover, I guess you can't blame them, but why take unethical advantage? Jewish women stop sticking your ring fingers at me, I have my weak points too.

She is a whore and makes me feel like a star. She has made advances in her chosen profession, having discovered how to hold patrons as long as she wants: never criticize them, keep your mouth shut. Always kiss them when they do something you like. I see her navy-blue hair pearl-white and cascaded, and scattered with rhinestones. Her voice twinkles and trembles. She sends out shocks of peach-colored paper.

26

ROY'S WIFE

TO TALK of Roy's Wife at all is to talk of towers. To show her at all is to show us showered with light. Her beauty is a beacon for us wretches when we are wretches and then can go shimmer.

To make her an Amazon—breastless—because she is supple. Put the power of prose in her pen. That she may sit grandly and we must look high up. That she is the Guinevere, fresh and flat-breasted. That she may come proudly and feathers sway as she walks. When she passes the air is perfumed to the extreme—with the special soap she washes her skin to make it clear and dry until it flakes. That sweet sulfur in her neck and clothes and ricochets around her apartment, clean and disreputable, when Roy is in jail. That I kneel to her and vow plumes to her. That my lips are painted fairytale red. I tether my griffin.

Griffon. Gryphon. I have lost the ability to spell this word definitely and for all time. I have lost the final essence of spelling it and now this animal will sail in the clouds of my mind, never to be bronze again, tongue that C's or S's.

She will lead me in the fight. She will swish my soul through Frisco waters, we will soar above the turrets. Her hand is on an ashtray, her hand is making me a potato-chip sandwich. Her mind is boiling us coffee. She belongs to the Acropolis but not as a slouchy caryatid. She is the Parthenon itself, when it was new. Or first in battle and I gilded her spear tip eyes. What is an aegis? It has snakes. Bonnie your aegis will writhe us home safely and the tips of your brown hair will touch our cheeks as we sleep.

She has sent for a bean, pea, and lentil cookbook to save money. She soaks a dish of beans overnight. I have bought her a little pot pipe. She sits crosslegged, straight back, eyes down, on a folded blanket smoking like Pocahontas. She makes caravans in her own apartment, stopping on the floor of different rooms from week to week. She travels light: her pot pipe, her blanket, a pillow that she sits on when she feels very Turkish, an ashtray, cigarettes with matches, and a full cup of black coffee. Her movements are smooth and laconic. I am absorbed watching her. Her dexterity is incredible to recount. She can smoke the smallest roach until it disappears —until it turns to a single spark on the tip of her finger which flares and vanishes—and I am not speaking of those uncouth hipsters who make a grand show of huffing and puffing the last tokes of a roach and then put it in their mouth and roll it around to make you think they love pot so much —no! Roy's Wife can take a roach these jerks would long since have swallowed as being too small even for handling with fingernails, calmly relight it with a match if it has gone out, and she even has time to accidentally drop it on the floor, recover it still lit, transfer it from hand to hand while looking at it like a jeweller and then smoke it slow till it vanishes. Ah! Those micromovements. And housewives of the world never fear for your carpets and bedspreads, because Roy's Wife will snatch a burning roach from thick grey pile faster than it has time to scorch a mark or smoke at all—and her calm blue eyes and straight long fingers move so slow they nearly stop—in that microsecond pulled out like taffy.

When she speaks her voice is high and silver.

27

PASTICHE OF THE GOLDEN FLOWER

HEAVEN CANNOT BE SEEN, for the two eyes are of it. Wherever the eye looks, the heart is directed also. The hen can hatch her eggs because her heart is always listening. She conducts the power of heat into the interior of the eggs with her hearing. Therefore a hen always has the attitude of listening with bent ear. The heart alone must be conscious of the flowing in and out of the breath, it must not be heard with the ears. One hears only what has no sound. One sees only that no shape is there. Can we wish for the Light to fall quite gently on the hearing? This question contains a secret meaning.

Curtain the eyes and the Light will stream in. It will begin to circulate in a wonderful way. When you begin to feel poisoned, put aside your knitting and give It all your attention. But when the work is so far advanced that secret confirmations are experienced, it does not matter if at the same time ordinary affairs are put into order, for one must fulfill his karma and do that which he doeth.

Too much cannot be demanded of the heart, and nor does the heart demand. The day goes too fast for him, he says the day is too short. He reads. They have their own park. The son died, so in honor of the son they built a park. They give him books, you should see the books, they weigh a ton. The

Hebrew books they don't let him take home. They have a heart, they know how much kids can carry.

Children, take heed! If for a day you do not practice meditation the force of Light trickles away. It leaves you, who knows whither? If you meditate only ten minutes you can set a thousand births at rest. This marvelous magic cannot be fathomed.

The spirit of a good man is a pure light air. When death comes it rushes out through the mouth and nose, rises upward and drifts to Heaven. "Silently in the morning thou fliest upward." But at the moment of death the spirit of a bad man trembles. It passes out through the cock and asshole, crystallizing downward. It sinks to Hell and becomes a demon.

Fire and light on the broken nose. Release is in the eye and fright. Flames press upward to lick the eye. Both eyes look out to the Mexican. Now if both eyes close and look in —that is the backward-flowing method. My finger traces an outward spiral around the belly button to the brown velvet cock standing under it like a pennant. If at the moment of release, the sperm is not allowed to flow outward, but is led back by the force of thought to penetrate the crucible of the heart, the petals of the Golden Flower fall open. The opening of the Golden Flower depends on the backward-flowing method.

Here are the signs of the Golden Bud opening. Here are the confirmations that come to you secretly. A feeling that the great Earth is a world of light and brilliancy. A sense of great gaiety as if intoxicated or freshly bathed. The objects around you are like ice and glassy jewels. The whole body fears neither storm nor frost. Pale gold coins fill the house, the steps are white jade. Red blood becomes milk. The fleshly body shines like silk or jade. The fragile flesh is gold and diamonds. The skin feels the presence of gods in the valley. The spirit pushes against Heaven, the body levitates, there is an uprush of Light. The Earth opens, a great terrace arises and upon it a Golden Being appears. Who can it be but Buddha? For Buddha is the Golden Saint of the Great Enlightenment.

28

THE MOUSE KING

I DON'T LIKE MOUSETRAPS or mousedrops that form at the little pricks of knocked-out mice. I don't like to see mice split or squeezed in two by traps. I love mice and don't like mousemeat. I don't like to see mice limp and dead from having been hurled to the floor. Then you have to poke a stick up their little asses and cram them down the side-winder's throat. I don't think anyone should be fed by force.

And yet I am the Eichmann of mice. One spring I was swarmed with mice, eight, nine, ten at once racing heavily on the floor and scuffling in the pantry. Ed Marshall was frightened, but I said, "Just a few baby mice playing tag, let them alone," and we went to bed. The next morning I was awakened by Ed Marshall raging in the kitchen. "Our oats, our rice, our beans," he screamed, "and a hole through the new loaf of bread, and half a box of crackers gone. And no more money for food, what will we do?" He was almost in tears. In fact a tear streamed down his cheek.

To understand his grief, you must know that Ed Marshall is wont to say, "I wouldn't mind a drop more of coffee— about that much." He waits patiently while his cup is filled to the brim. "Do you have a little roll or something, a piece of bread maybe, to go with the coffee? . . . I'll have just a

97

taste of that cheese. . . . Is that a new kind of apple you just bought?" But though he pays mouth-service to "tasting" something or "trying it out," to him food is food, a vast homogeneous mush not solid and not liquid, for the sheer mass of which his internal hunger has always been so boundless, that his sense of taste never had a chance to mature. The result is that when he asks to taste something as a strategem for engulfing it—and he always asks for whatever he sees or thinks you have on hand—he invariably says "very good" as it vanishes. He means: "It's very good to devour something."

And now the mice were still playing tag in the kitchen, oblivious to his roars of indignation. I tried to console him. "Now, now," I said, "you go on back to bed, and I'll figure out a way to get rid of the mice." I sat down and thought. I thought and I thought, but to no avail. There was no money for traps or poison, and I don't like to kill animals anyway. But it was true they had to go. It was them or us. I was at an impasse. To help my mind associate more freely, I smoked a marijuana cigarette. I was watching a pair of mice chase each other about, when I noticed how slowly they seemed to be moving. "I'll bet I can catch them," I said to myself. All my embarrassment at stalking animals had vanished. I followed a mouse all around the room, until it was in a corner. As I feinted with my foot, I reached down quickly and caught it. Victory! But now that I held it, what could I do? Certainly not walk down five flights of stairs to release it, nor flush it down the toilet ignobly. There had to be a simple final solution. I decided to throw it out the window, for if it were destined to live perhaps a roc would snatch it, and if it were destined to die, it would die a quick death. So I strode into the bedroom holding it high above my head.

There was no righteous reflex
    From Ed Marshall in bed
(Who says the literal name of God
    In prayer at least once every five minutes)
He didn't jump up seeing the mouse in my fingers
    And shout, "Open the window!"
He said, "A mouse has just been caught,"
    And looked at it holy and blessed it
While it peeped like a chick in my fingers
    And tried to bite me
    But its jaw was too little.

There was no righting reflex
    When I threw the mouse from my window
As high as I could and watched it arc down
    Maybe it was too young or scared
To have a righting reflex
    Instead it turned over and over
    Slowly in the empty space.

In less than two hours I had caught and hurled nine mice
into the sky. That very night Huncke paid us a visit, and I
told him the whole story of the pogrom. "And I will probably be brought before a mouse tribunal," I concluded.

Just then I saw a mouse on the kitchen table and jumped
at this chance to show off. First I showed it to Huncke—
pointed it out to him across the room—the red and green
stones on my ring gleaming—then I said laughingly (my
performance begun) "I will catch it," and I stalked into the
kitchen, hovered over the kitchen table admiring pot for
pulling out time enough for me to cope with mouse nervous-
ness—it was sniffing every inch of the table, and I was digging every sniff and dart, and a roach was crawling on a tea
chest—partners in crime—and at the right moment my

hand dropped silently on the mouse. I could feel the movement of tiny bones under fur and smell its musk. I brought it to Huncke triumphantly, and showed him its tail, which stuck out from my fingers. "Well you said it squeals," he said grudgingly, "I want the whole show." "O.K. listen," I retorted, and held the mouse to his ear wishing for a squeal to crown my success and possibly pressing it ever so slightly, and sure enough it squealed, and I was the King of Mice. Then Huncke said with mock callousness, "Why don't you throw it out the window?" I said I would and left the room. When I returned he asked what I had done with it, and I told him. He seemed astonished. "Really? No, you didn't, did you? People like you think that animals don't have feelings, but I think they feel things like us. Wow, what a terrible way to die." He tried to express what a mouse must feel falling through space and brought wet stars of pity for mice to my eyes. I was holding my hands out before me, limp and high, so I wouldn't touch anything before I could wash them. I told Huncke, "You make me feel like licking these hands instead of washing the mousedirt off."

29

RECIPROCITY

THERE WAS A TIME when Huncke and Allen lived in the same building, which I used to visit grinning because if one wasn't home I could visit the other—and even if I was headed toward Huncke's on the top floor, how could I pass Allen's door without knocking? And yet Huncke would cross-examine me to determine whether I had come especially to visit him, or was visiting him because Allen wasn't home, or was visiting him incidentally, on the way to or from Allen's. He grew so fearful of being considered a sidekick of Allen's, that he subjected all his visitors to the same interrogation, and he even descended to craft in order to trap you into admitting that your visit to him wasn't exclusive after all. For example he would ask with ambiguous urgency if you had seen Allen—as if Allen had been looking for you or as if Huncke himself were admonishing you for visiting him without also visiting Allen, who would be hurt if he knew you were actually in the building and didn't stop by.

"No Huncke, I came to visit you. Now I may fall in on Allen later, if it's not too late, just to say hello, but I came all the way over here to spend a few hours with you—if you'll have me that long." Appeals like this cut no ice with Huncke, and the only real solution was to pretend that he and Allen lived in different parts of the city, and to call on each accordingly, returning home if the one you set out to see wasn't in.

Sheeper indulged Huncke in his wish to be treated as an absolutely unique being who could neither substitute for anyone else nor be substituted for, because Sheeper too was obsessed with his own uniqueness, and the uniqueness of things and events, even though he knew he was up against a strong determination on the part of Mother Nature to make her human children as uniform as possible, varying them just enough to insure the survival of the group despite environmental vicissitudes. Even as a child, Sheeper used to shake his little fist at any attempt to make him conform to the standards of behavior followed by other children, and he spent many years of his adulthood devising engines of war against Nature and trying to raise palaces of the mind that would put the structure of the universe to shame. "O.K.," he used to say, "so I can't quite smash atoms yet or make stars explode, but look at these plans," and he used to flip the pages of his notebook in your face. "There my friend, there on page gimel I have sketched a castle more glorious than any snow-capped mountain or Protean grotto carved out by the sea. So it can't quite be built in this era, so what."

Sheeper is so obsessed with uniqueness that he refuses to recognize the most common sociological facts, for example that fifty per cent of all marriages take place between individuals born within fifty miles of each other. Sheeper would like to believe that men comb the four corners of the world searching for brides, pulling up tent flaps and tearing off face veils. And sometimes he just ignores the fact that all cocks are alike and want to come off, and honors the cock of a lover he especially admires by dressing it in an evening gown, till he is brought back to his senses by cries of anguished impatience or the cock itself wrecks everything by raping the couturier.

How else is Sheeper obsessed with uniqueness? Trying to clank the irrevocable sentence, all this worry about commas, he's got eternity on the brain like a tumor. Dreams of the one final lover who will never defect. To cross out the accidental. To create an art of the Brain alone. Ach, and all the accidental objects in the room invade the prose. Yet he knows he met Shadrow by being assigned the seat behind him in school, an accident of the alphabet. And he knows that wherever he has hitchhiked, displaying himself and all he stands for on the highway, he has always been picked up, that in the poof poof poof of cars on a highway there will always be one man who will slow down for him, in Soledad or outside of Poughkeepsie, and get out of his car yet to help Sheeper put his duffel bag inside, and not make any demands for conversation or anything else, so that he can take out his notebook and write for four hours, knowing from the ghost of a smile on the driver's face that he is hip to his own good effect, and when the time comes to part and Sheeper grows effusive with gratitude ("I have never been treated with such . . . with so . . ."), the driver cut him short, saying, "Glad to have had the company," and disappears onto a crooked dirt road off the highway. That we are all brothers is *not* accidental, so travel light. Sell all your books and read only others'.

Love your neighbors like yourself. They will do. *Anyone will do.* Don't pick your friends too closely, it's like carrying a decimal accurate to units out ten places. People are completely interchangeable, and you will find someone who will serve for anything. Don't hesitate to travel for fear of leaving close friends behind, you will make new ones, and new mamas and lovers crop up everywhere.

One man is tall like me, another is queer, another has my
skin disease. I join hands with the whole human race.

Then if only our nervous systems were connected (not
just our unconscious collective) which obsesses me too. Instead of having to learn so slowly how to be kind. For example, look at that big boy throwing snowballs at the bus
you are in. Just when a snowball hits your window thud,
wouldn't it be nice if an equal and opposite snowball hit him
thud in the face? Oh the lungers we spit on the pavement
rebel! "I refuse to be used to spread your diseases!" Our jaws
drop in astonishment! The sputum gathers itself into glob-
ules, mimics the sound of us clearing our throat, and cata-
pults back in our mouth!

Ah, if loving someone and being loved in return were the
very same act, and unrequited love a logical impossibility.
To know no fear of being loved without loving in return—
and knowing he will leave again without leaving a note behind. You get hints of this marvelous world, little frustrating
glimpses of it—in suddenly seeing your whole body nude in
a mirror, in falling in love with a man if you are a man (or
with a human being if you are a human being!), in states
of such exalted intimacy, like very high sex, when the two
poles are one, that the pleasure you give seems to sweep
through your body.

30

HUNCKE

HUNCKE SAYS, "I used to be the youngest in the group I ran around with. Now I'm the oldest. Well that's life." But I cannot believe that Huncke's age ever mattered, or that he was ever very different from the way he is now, agelessly reminiscing about times gone by: "When I lived on the Square I used to have a friend and sidekick named Jack Melody . . ." "The only time I ever saw anybody cut bread like that was in Wales, in a town called Newport, a few miles below Cardiff . . ." "I was first turned on to opium by a half-Chinese sailor, or ex-sailor, who ran a small bar in Havana—I don't remember his name I'm ashamed to say, and I liked him a lot . . ." He must have been a secret wise old man when he was fifteen and his skin glowed like his eyes—those eternally adolescent eyes that everyone remembers as blue though they are hazel. For their cosmetic care alone Babylonian kings would have accorded him the use of drugs—opium to tighten his eyes into shrapnel and cannabis to make his pupils black roses. He must always have dropped offhand remarks that shudder through the ages, and he must have been a wise old man at fifteen when he sat at the dinner table with his family and a messenger came in with a bouquet of roses from an admirer.

I cannot believe that Huncke ever talked about sex any

differently from the way he talks about it now, as something joyful but no longer indulged in, and he seldom closes a story's paragraph more poignantly than when he says, "and then we stripped and balled." How did he talk about sex when he was fifteen, as the romantic activity of a childhood then gone forever? Or did his voice and mind add fifty years to the act that had taken place the night before?

I am sure that Huncke has been the same since he was born, and to an extent Marrows bears me out, for the passages which deal with Huncke in Marrows' first book, which covers a period twenty to thirty years ago, are fair descriptions of Huncke today. And in that book Marrows has an old-timer say, in speaking of a still earlier time shrouded in myth, "Huncke was a beautiful kid when he first came to New York. The trouble is, he lost his looks."

This remark is sharp, and in fact Marrows portrayed Huncke unsympathetically. For example, Marrows wrote: "Soon I was buying his drinks and meals, and he was hitting me for 'smash' (change) at regular intervals. He did not have a habit at this time. In fact, he seldom got a habit unless someone else paid for it. . . . It would not have occurred to him to pay the rent himself. He had lived in other people's apartments all his life." And Huncke answered back gracefully in a little red notebook now in my possession: "It is true—I have lived in other people's apartments a good many times, but I have had a few of my own which were great enough for me to feel that Bill wasn't quite fair and that in summing me up so narrowly he gives clear evidence of a certain smugness which is hardly becoming to an author of such rugged realism as that found in *Adder*."

In spite of his portrait in *Adder*, Huncke has always spoken of Marrows affectionately. Think of this image, of Marrows drunk and asleep, angelic and delicate skin, of

Huncke sitting on the edge of the bed to admire him, of Marrows waking and trying to make love, and Huncke all wise and coy saying, "Aw Bill, now I know you're drunk," and Huncke laughs again as he relates it, his eyes all shining with being desired.

One day I said to him, "I've been doing research on you, Huncke. Rereading Marrows." He said, "I have never been happy with his treatment of me. He makes me out a scrawny leech or parasite—and while I know I sometimes—I mean if someone has a little bread—"

"But you don't do it—ah—maliciously."

"Exactly."

The truth is that Huncke puts the touch on you only for what he thinks you can afford or are willing to give. Perhaps he asks for a little more than you can afford—as an insurance—but he always settles quickly for whatever you offer. However he makes you feel slightly guilty for not having given him what he requested, and if you are in a giving mood he extracts as much as he can. For example he may ask you for money, telling you he is out of bread, out of milk, out of coffee. You may say, "I have no money but I can give you a sandwich." He accepts that gratefully, but while he is eating he may ask, "Do you mind if I fix a sandwich for Kinky, who I want to fall in on, and who hasn't had anything to eat for days?"

Actually Huncke's moral code is very strict, and he will ask for things only of people he considers more fortunate than himself—which is nearly everyone. Whatever money he comes into he squanders at once, and so he is always down and out. And perhaps that is just as well because, as he says, whenever he comes into bread he gets busted. Sometimes he says it this way: "Just when I start collecting a decent wardrobe I am busted."

His "wardrobe"—and all other personal effects—are put together from the one or two articles he keeps for himself out of each of the suitcases he steals from parked automobiles. So he lives, when he is not in jail, surrounded by golden manicure sets, big bottles of fairy cologne to splash himself with, and silk pajamas striped like window awnings. And what can he feel when he gets out of bed in the afternoon, unrolls a pair of socks acquired the night before, and a slip of paper zigzags down to the floor—he picks it up and reads this note, writ in a woman's hand:

> I'm everywhere
> I love you
> XXX

Coming down off amphetamine, Huncke grunts and he groans. His lips swell. His nose runs. He sleeps all day, farting at intervals. And when he's not asleep he's bitching. "What? You don't have any cornflakes? Well what *do* you have? Look at how swollen my hands are. I hope that coffee isn't for me, you know I don't like glass cups. What will I tell Kinky on Sunday? He gave me a double sawbuck to score, and I lost it or blew it all, I can't even remember. And my hemorrhoids have started bleeding again, do you have a tube of Preparation H and a clean pair of shorts? At this point my life is so fucked up I can't even think. You're looking at my legs as if you never saw sores before. Well they're from scrubbing myself in the shower to get the scabies off. Scabies are microscopic animals that live on sores. Joan and I discovered them under a magnifying glass. Now don't cock your eyes like that, it's a proven fact. I wish I had a copy of the Mayan Codices, because I could show them to you. We actually identified the little beasts in the Mayan Codices, and that's why Joan originally went to Mexico, to do research on them. My fingertips are sore. What will I tell the parole officer on Monday? He was nice as he could be, but he warned me if I didn't have a job by Monday I would go back to jail. What will I tell 'unemployment' next Tuesday? How am I going to explain why I didn't report last week? No money, no clothes, not a particle of shmeeaz to help me come down with, and you have the nerve to send away a guy who might have laid a bag on me, I'll never forgive you for that, what will become of me? And stop hinting that I should go back to bed in your little sneaky way, I'll go when I'm ready. I just lie there writhing and can't fall asleep."

I do not mind giving further examples of Huncke's petulance and little temper storms, for even if I listed them all, that man would still stand high as cliff flames, and those eyes would not lose a wisp of their mercury vapor. Sometimes his eyes are like grubs in his skull, cold living beings you come to notice are pulsing slowly, and then as Huncke turns his attention to someone who is talking, they hatch into darning-needles hovering in front of the speaker (Huncke listens with his eyes), and they make a whole series of sewing-machine stitches of information before darting back home to the brainpan and inner intelligence headquarters.

One night he forced me to make him a bacon and tomato sandwich as his price for cooperating enough to be taken in a taxi to a mental hospital as the last resort and excuse for his failure to have reported to his parole officer for weeks, and a bench warrant had already been issued, and the sympathetic doctor at the hospital had warned us to be there before eleven that night, when he, the doctor, would go off admission duty for the week, and it was 10:35 when Huncke balked as we were going out the front door, sat down, said he was hungry and wouldn't go a step farther without being fed, and insisted on a bacon and tomato sandwich because every prisoner gets to choose his last meal before being led to execution.

Another time I innocently asked a friend of his what kind of work he did, and Huncke exploded, accusing me of the worst prying ill manners he had ever encountered, and he vowed he would never again bring any of his friends over, especially a prostitute named Flory who did a little fencing on the side, and whom he had wanted me to meet; but now he would never think of submitting her to the kind of inquisition I practiced. "My friends are very sensitive about how they earn their living. And I'm not going to bring her over here and put her in the center of a whole group of intellectual people who can come on, and I know how they come on, with their pointed questions, and there isn't another whore in the crowd."

But time and time again I have seen him quiet little crackles of hostility in those around him with love and patience, not as a cunning way to keep the peace, but because he believes enmity to be an improper state, as much his own responsibility to redress as the wrongdoers'. And I have seen him befriend those men who are to me pariahs— who have sold out or copped out or want to stop up the life and art that come streaming from souls. He is always sorry for them and thinks there is a chance they can be reformed. Off the page and out of the book we kick the trouble he (therefore) always brings with him, and the malicious mischief he sometimes engages in. These are the dry leaves we rake off the page and burn or forget, to have a book, or live with men at all. And should I have to suffer the tragedy and disaster Huncke always brings with him, or the beautiful boys he tows like an old queen but is unable to make (and makes me curse my innards if I should so much as smile at

one, that Huncke's pride should not be hurt or jealousy
aroused), or boys retracing lonely steps on littered sidewalks
looking for God knows what lost ring or wristwatch, or
fortyish husbands in alcoholic sleep curled up outside the
tenement door their wives won't open?

And although we are born with the knowledge that once
we penetrate each other's fears we will arrive at the spot
where the nest is feathered for all mankind, still death forces
stay me from answering soul-searching letters for months. It
is a disaster to be human, and for that, goaded by the little
compassion I was born with, I strove for art—the only place
we can win. Art lets us be the best and truest that we are,
all drugs do. I always get stranded waiting for a bus on the
coldest days. —As at certain moments Utaemon's tragedy—
the secret personal tragedy (who knows what it is?) of that
great Kabuki dancer who in a lifetime of acting has never
betrayed a leg withered six inches shorter than the other by
infantile paralysis—fits the tragedy of The Courtesan so absolutely as to make me ashamed of the bullshit I live in along
with the other swine when I am not dreaming.

The moon gives me a hard-on. Which spoke out loud
reaps a short Huncke riff. "I've jacked off in the moonlight.
Many a time. I like to jack off in the moonlight, in fact I
like to jack off period. By myself or with others, and I've
jacked off other inmates under circumstances you wouldn't
believe possible, like across two feet of concrete between
cell doors."

If there were a Saviour, Huncke would preach Holy Gos-
pel, and if dead souls could speak, he would fall into trances.
Well there are drugs, that I know, and he turneth us on.
"You're sure you don't want a taste?" he says, drawing the

junk up into his dropper. "You're sure now? It's good shit. I can leave you a drop in the spoon. Well, you can have the cotton if you change your mind."

I crooked my index finger covered with rings and said, "Huncke, you would turn your own mother on."

"Would turn her on," he said, "I did turn her on." He quickly added, "Only to pot. She didn't like it too much, made me rub her side, under the arm. She was afraid her heart would stop beating. She was hip in many ways. Used to chaperone me on dates with my boyfriends."

No one knows anything in this world as well as Huncke knows the anatomy of his arm veins. But this time his luck was bad. First he tried a tiny vein in his upper arm without success, and muttered, "I'll get you some day you little bastard." Then he tried a tough, rubbery vein in his lower arm one, two, three, four times, but the vein kept eluding the needle, by slipping to one side of it or the other, once the skin had been punctured. "That one is a roller," Huncke explained; "but even so I don't usually have to probe this much." Then he came clean: "Guess I'm showing off a little . . . aw shucks." Either he is always pointing to junk, or else I cannot see through it to what he is pointing.

Huncke is no sooner out of jail, than he is hooked again and turns to theft. He is apprehended in a matter of months. Never was a criminal more petty and unsuccessful. And then he is always trying to draw his friends into witnessing his pathetic courtroom appearances, into raising bail for him, into writing him letters to keep up his morale. Why bother with him at all?

Because he is a Beauty Trap and the finest storyteller my spirit has ever lifted to. He always says he relates just what he remembers, but he picks and clips unconsciously, transposes and condenses on each retelling, till his stories conform wholly to the beautiful configuration of his mind. His tales light up with compassion the most blighted and bizarre personalities, and he can portray these unfortunates with such flash and splendor that they turn into creatures of gorgon beauty before your eyes, or their beauty, pathos, and horror may jar unresolved in your mind for several days afterwards, finally condensing into beauty pure and clear, but with that slight jangle or derangement to it, that fixes it forever.

In telling a story he becomes a spirit risen high above his mortal body—risen high and drifting even higher in the empty space. He talks through his flesh below like a ventriloquist. It may be Huncke's voice box which says "I", but it is that high astral body who holds our ear, and who owns every fault and sin of the man below relevant to the complete truthful telling of the tale, without the slightest shame or dodge. Ah and those small incidental confessions the spirit calls no special attention to in passing are like incandescent shrines of light falling on the wretch's head below. Huncke beams, shriven, while the narrating spirit pushes on, unaware of the magic it has wrought.

31

GUM

Roy's wife would never accept a half-stick of gum, as mutilations bugged her. I tore all my sticks of gum in half before she came over, to keep the juicy secret of Spearment gum torn or whole to myself. Jonas absentmindedly slipped a stick of Spearmint gum from the pocket of a vest he had lately affected. Did he chew it, put it back, or offer it to me? He kept it in his hand for a moment, staring it goodbye. Then he held it out to me with a generosity which was frankly alarming. "If you don't want it now, save it for later."

Dipping old gum into sugar to bring back its flavor fails. This pseudodox epidemical to children has disappointed millions of wet little tongues. However, chewing bread with old gum to make it soft again works. Grape gum gives a person the most interesting breath in the world. When I was a child, Delaware Punch was my cup of tea, for tasting like grape gum and not being fizzy. I could never understand why people drank drinks that stung and prickled their tongues.

Do you remember blowing a big bubble-gum bubble till just before it broke and then blowing it still bigger to break and fall down flabby? How numb we have grown. Do you remember when the touch of your own hand on your face or thigh was enough to give you a hard-on?

Children can be made to shine like jewels by brushing their hair and washing their faces and giving them kisses and squeezing little shoulders. They are sweeter and more lovey than chittering chipmunk kittens and I think included when an old lady in a Quaker meetinghouse prays for the bones of tiny animals.

To kidnap children! To feed them testosterone like candy to close their epiphyses! They will never grow up. But they grow up in sex, and so much the better. To be loved by a six-year-old with a big man's cock (twelve-inch salami). Doctor is this a perverse desire?

"Are you the doctor in charge? The nurse outside told me I could see you. I have just one question to ask, and you won't have to give me a blood test. About ten days ago I spent the night with someone who is being treated for syphilis of the throat. The party said there was no danger of my contracting the disease. We kissed and nothing more. About a week ago I developed a slight sore throat and wonder if you would look at it and tell me if there is any possibility that it might be syphilis."

"Was it a male?"

"Why do you ask? Doctor are you trying to pass a moral judgment on me?"

According to Darwinian theories homosexuality should have wiped itself out the instant it showed its . . . gentle interesting face. What progeny to inherit your queerness if all you can do is suck cocks? But it sticks to the race like gum. Are we doomed with rebirth forever my dears? Answer me that, O Master.

I answered this auntie, don't cry about having no children my dear, now now you've got a karmic fertility that would put a shad to shame. A dozen queer babies will be born with the flames of your funeral pyre flashing. Right O Master?

A boy veering in the queer direction should be encouraged to go that way as far as he can, for to live wholly untainted by female intrigues and tyranny. And little girls should be encouraged in the same respective direction, for to ply their poisonous arts on each other.

Here is a tale for children, called "The Black Little Girls": During recess two little girls were standing together by a drinking fountain. The love between them mounted uncontrollably. Suddenly they touched tongues. Every day they would play together after school, hopping scotch or skipping rope, or they would walk hand in hand, looking for discarded gum to chew. That's all.

Here is a tale for older children, called "The Octopus": Two friends, Mrs. Carp and Miss Oliver, travelling together on the astral plane, decided to visit the bottom of the sea. They believed they arrived there and saw an enormous octopus floating about the wreckage on the ocean bed. Not long after, the two ladies had a jealous quarrel over a certain Miss Pike, to whom, a day later, Mrs. Carp bit her former friend's back like this: "My dear, don't have anything to do with that young lady, because she goes about telling people that she is beloved by an archangel who kisses her on the lips, but I have seen the archangel who follows her about trying to influence people through her, and it has the shape of an octopus."

Here is a tale for children, called "The Little Boy Who Couldn't Wait to Masturbate": There was a little boy who couldn't wait to masturbate. Five minutes before he got home, the most delicious thoughts would start rubbing his little pisser, and soon he would feel a familiar pressure in the front part of his pants. He hurried home as fast as he could.

A mother sprinkles warm sand on her young son's belly. He has fallen at her feet exhausted from swimming. A lithe nude Porto Rican, almost certainly a girl, is taking a bath across the courtyard. I am hypnotized by his or her limbs and keep hoping he will shift position so I can ascertain his sex. It is either a tall late-maturing boy—no pubic hair—not a woman because there are no breasts—or else a tall pre-pubescent girl. As I am admiring the marble thighs, hoping for a lucky turn in the torso, suddenly that turn is made, and I see I am looking at a girl. A little boy in pajamas blows a fog spot on the window pane early one morning while his mother fixes breakfast. A wooden top is in his hand. At another window several half-dressed children romp in the kitchen, you can see their legs and white underwear flash by the curtain split.

According to the Master, minds have more protein than spring lamb or veal.

32

TRIPE

SHEEPER AND ALLEN are eating tripe soup in a Greek restaurant. Sheeper notices a toothpick behind Allen's ear, seizes it and like a madman starts picking his teeth. Did a mist of dental enamel like white rose tips on the great placoderm sprout? The Lord enable me to shift. On Thursday Huncke took me out to one of those sad, tinny Thanksgiving dinners, $1.99 and on ill-gotten gains. By Sunday he was back in the Tombs. Shift to the Grace Hope and Charity Mission, run by three dikes from Wichita. They preach the Gospel and no one comes up. They pass out sandwiches and everyone comes up. Someone says, "Lookit them broads. I wonder if they ever been screwed." Hope pulls that man out of the line, nearly wrenching off his arm. "You," she screeches, "you can't have a sandwich."

By studying bull-dikes and queens I come to the conclusion what type of men and women they think themselves to be. I am sick and tired of Tallulah Bankhead queens, they drive ye Mary Pickfords out of circulation. Tall Gary Cooper dikes are comely and well hung. I wish I had a tall G.C. dike to bring home the bacon. Yummy.

Jewish dietary laws that make you feel rotten if you eat a piece of bacon are good practice for vegetarian precepts that make you feel horrid if you eat a hot dog. When the Poet stayed with me he made my whole apartment smell piggy. At first I thought it was bacon fat burning, but then I saw him do it with butter. It was eerie. He added something gentile to the very foods in my icebox.

Anyone who comes live with me has to eat my Jewish foods—most of which I refused to taste as a child—I got sick of all that Jewish lipsmacking. Recently I began to eat them as an affectation and now—and now dear friends—my lips are wet with fish stews and goos.

"Yass my dear he eats like a bird, yass yass my dear Yetta, only God alone knows vat I been through with his health, oy if only I had a penny out of every dollar I spent on him in the clinics." She used to drag me around to the clinics which I hated like poison, and make me feel rotten for costing her the 25¢ registration fee—that woman won't roast in hell she'll sizzle and explode in flames like burning fat—and she used to ask me every morning how I felt, and I had to say all right in a certain melancholy way so that she could sigh, "Vell if you don't feel too good, I'll take you to the clinic."

"Yass my dear he eats like a bird, you know his teacher said he vas a pocket-size dictionary, he's so particular and I have to treat him like a little prince and cook him special food all the time, he's allergic to so many things my dear. I have to give him goat's milk a half a dollar a quart and we eat hamburger not him he gets a lamb chop."

We are eating dinner, my mother is staring at me. Slowly and carefully I cut the gristle off a chunk of stewed meat. I push the gristle to the edge of the plate. "Vat's the matter now?" my mother screams.

"There was a piece of gristle on my meat."

"That's no gristle, that's meat!" My mother picks up the gristle with her fingers and eats it. Along with the horrible sound of gristle being crunched come the words: "Veins in the liver, little black bumps in the smashed potatoes, grains of sand in the middle of a fresh pear, I'll be goddamned if I cook another meal for that kid, let him starve and go hungry, I'll give him twenty cents a day and let him eat in the automat." As for the meat she fed me, I'll be doing time below.

In hell flocks and flocks of lambs and calves, bleating and lowing and nuzzling your hand, will frolic about you but this tender pastorale is marred by the horrible mutilations each animal suffers, one with its belly ripped open and half its baby calf-liver gone, another with the iridescent blue of a lamb shank showing, a third with its chest wall sunk in and Wiener Schnitzel missing—each one minus that particular cut of its body you ate in your lifetime. And when I think of the half chickens bleeding and dying and yet affectionately trying to flop as close to you as possible, I get sick. Even innocents who were forced to eat meat will be visited by these gamboling crippled wraiths. Let me digress from the text to describe the strangest confrontation in all the subterranean realms—it is of a man with his own wraith, the man having just died of torture, the wraith with a slice of calf muscle missing. You see certain North American Indians made shish-kebab of strips of flesh cut from a live prisoner, and forced the prisoner to partake of his own roasted self. "Just a little little bit," he would screamingly implore. Other savages, I forget where now, keep meat fresh for weeks by not slaughtering the cow but hacking off a slice of rump whenever they get hungry and then slapping a leaf poultice back on the wound. Golden Horde warriors who couldn't dismount for a Coca-Cola sucked blood from a horse neck vein quickly opened.

An Arab, teaching you the Arabic for different cuts of meat, points them out on his own body, and for this lack of self-deception he will suffer less in hell. If you must eat meat it is more virtuous to slaughter it yourself, more virtuous to eat it in its original form rather than ground up or as sausage, more virtuous to eat it raw or rare, and more virtuous to eat the visceral portions. It is always much better to acknowledge that you are eating a killed sentient being. Traces of the animal's soul linger to its dead flesh like vitamins, and are destroyed by cooking and mechanical processing. Visceral meats are much richer in soul than skeletal meats. It is that little bit of soul ingested that makes you feel queasy—and the more nauseous the better for you—for it will actually squeak out in your favor on Doomsday. If you have to eat meat eat ears! Eat eyes! Eat cow lips with fine hairs! Eat her tongue and brains and all the shining red and yellow glands inside her! Eat udder! Eat the heart the lungs the liver! Lick your fingers after smoothing out raw liver! Let the succulent camel suckling boiled in its mother's milk melt in your mouth! Sup on all four cow stomachs and yards of shiny white spaghetti bowels on which you can see blood vessels play chopped up into tripe! Tripe and its textures and layers and colors grey white and golden! The goo! The bristling papillae! The honeycomb patches! O all the pale secrets of fat cow digestion laid bare in your soup to be eaten!

33

AUTHORS

ARABIA DESERTA took ten years to write, and you can see Doughty pushing up like a dwarf or troll to shore up the prose. He stands like an Atlas. And because we trust a man of his stature, we let ourselves be sent to the dictionary a hundred times. His disciple T.E. Lawrence tried to send us ten times, but we refused to go. For we cannot trust an author's usages whose prose is used to bluff, impress or lie. But the strain or pose shall strain out the lies, not be them. Readers see through prose like glass, so why lie? There is nothing wrong at all with a masquerade or intricate Moorish façade, so long as it is used to speak behind, not to bamboozle, but Lawrence lets bits of honesty show through the belle prose to make us believe it is backed up by honesty everywhere. I doubt that it is. And I doubt that Lawrence—or anyone—is capable of a sin or crime a full confession wouldn't shrive. So what remains not entirely hidden behind the grille of the *Seven Pillars of Wisdom* is cowardice.

Read Edward Dahlberg but pay no attention to anything he says. He is so critical and cantankerous, so grum, small, and jealous, that if you took him at all seriously he would drive you as batty as he is. The quotations he burdens his work with are never to the point, and, as he is incapable of placing two sentences in logical order, such a thing as a quiet, scholarly paragraph let alone essay or chapter is outside his reach. But he is *the* poet of sentence design, and the quirk that shocks you with delight in the half-dozen books he has left behind is not an accident nor the inkling of an army of virtues the thought of which staggers the imagination, but itself is the hand-tended blossom. What rose shine to stumble on a sentence of his so filled with helium you squeak like a mouse tumbling back and forth anywhere in five thousand years while doing the eternity samba in the pansy bahianas of Carmen Miranda the Brazilian cadaver— what rose shine in the midst of his usual thorny bramble of Marx Brothers scholarship and scrambled invective. As a matter of fact I like this glitter and have thrown myself at his feet, for he is a great pure writer in the sense that he will sacrifice any meaning however important he may have made it out to be for any flourish or conceit, and he would sell his soul to the devil and mine too for the power to write one unalterably beautiful sentence. Read him for vocabulary too, though he never coins words, his motto being "Rob graves don't make babies."

Graham Greene (for example) is an intelligent man, but—! What is it that interests these brain creeps, working out all the different things some mythical ideal of theirs would *think* of, and the man they make up is not my ideal.

> *Shipsey. Reichardt.*
> *Dunlop. Stockwell.*
> *The vast mausoleums.*
> *I should not speak ill of the dead*

Or their families.

I brought the notebook
To soak what it could
And I lay down in the shade.

The ants played
Over my map and notebook.

Have you ever wondered about Melville's sex life? I know
graduate students do, but I have a special non-academic right
to wonder, since I took my notebook to soak what it could at
Melville's grave. Did Melville ever make it with anyone
body to body? I say no even though I know he must have
fucked his wife at least five times since I saw four grave-
stones of his children and an odd marker of a fifth child
buried in California. I say no even though *Moby-Dick* ranks
with *Philosophie dans le Boudoir* for high undiluted sex to
the point where we scream for mercy, Mary. (And did he
know the work of Sade?) But the sex in *Moby-Dick* has had
its orgasm stolen completely away. We have a world of
young lovey men with obvious hard-ons we never hear
about from Melville's lips direct. He is a true closet queen.
You can hear his breath catch at the thick curve visible
through the tight bell-bottom trousers. (Lower, dip your
eyes lower, don't stop at the first sight of hair on the belly,
force your eyes down, dammit.)

Sometimes I think he never really found out how lovely
a boy's cock is, but fucked his wife dutifully or just to get
his rocks off. Maybe love was never consummated for him
in his life or work—if he didn't make it with boys—and
I'm not talking about cock itch but rosy boy body love. Or
rosy girl body love (phony democratic device we queer writers seem stuck with since Whitman). And by body I mean

to say Mind shining, which takes place in your cock as well as your partner's. For example two friends of mine should not have had to blow each other so laboriously, with such whews, gurgles, and bone cracks one night when the full moon shone so brightly, for there is no work to sex when you are queer for Mind. I think Melville worked very hard in bed with his wife. He huffed and he puffed. *Moby-Dick* is like a mountain range with all the tops cut off. Was the censorship deliberate Herman you wise old queen?

When I first met Charles I thought, O great God a Gargantua! A Pantagruel! A whale! A walrus among men! Great God did Melville have him in mind—in the back of some old black ledger? His tusks rise up from the steamy brine ten feet ahead of him. Above I hear the whirr and boom of gull cries, and down below my mother cries, "What's a goddam walrus doing in the bathtub?" Throw him a fish! O throw him a fish! (Or throw him a piece of Duncan's poetry—chunks of whale fat—thick curls and flourishes—can't see the bum for the blubber.)

O great bursts of gas he is a grampus! A house! A cow or barn! A Major Hoople or Mighty Mouse! O.K. black mountain, soon come the caterpillars.

It was time for him to go. He sighed and glanced into the heavy silver hand mirror he always carried with him. From its handle he unscrewed a thin silver blade coated with black dust and pinpoints of light. And with his hand like a bat flying a loop he drew the blade right and left across his eyeballs and screwed it back into its scabbard. He stood up. A kimono sleeve fell over the mirror in his hand, but when he lifted his arm for the sleeve to fall away, that same hand was holding instead of the mirror a thick yellowed manuscript. He laid it on my desk and said, "I began this book in the slums of New York (O San Francisco of my dreams!), jumping from a scaffold erected by the Rotten Hangmaster, and, having fled for the book's sake from the Statue of Liberty to the Pillars of Hercules on an umber carpet hurtling between two lovers (men I mean and not cities), I finished it in Tangier on the Barbary coast, in a whitewashed room where silk flowers bloomed on my slippers." And he vanished in a cloud of perfume so thick it made me cough. As an old friend I had promised to prepare the manuscript of his book for publication. I did not add a word, simply arranged what he had written in a form I believe he would have found natural. My most difficult task was to treat certain passages whose truth or glamour was invisible to me as if they were true. I am indebted to the American Soybean Foundation for the grant which has made this work possible.

The author seems to have been queer or at the very least bisexual. (And thus surely eligible for a Great American Authorship, in fact more than eligible, since the newly lowered requirements include spiritual bisexuals with no questions asked. You no longer have to submit proof that you have literally committed unspeakable acts with your application to that august college.) But I, who am an ordinary man, my vices not protected by the Muse, owe it to the public to state that I have never been tempted by the passions described in this book.

> Let no man thinke, that herein I stand with *Lucian* or hys devilish disciple *Aretino the One and Onlie,* in defence of execrable and horrible sinnes of forbidden and unlawful fleshlinesse.

A few years ago the cadavers who worked at Time, Loot,

and Fortune used to apologize by claiming they were boring from within, or were saving enough bread to work on their books and paintings in peace, or that all jobs in the U.S. were just as immoral and so what did it matter. This year an increase in truthfulness can be noted among them. They are wailing, "We were already dead. For the dead one graveyard is as good as another, why not Time's?"

The whole purpose and plan of librarians is to hang on to books. To keep them in prison and out of our hands. I bluffed and badgered a librarian into showing me a Beethoven manuscript—a sketch for the Trio in B Flat Major. That scrawl of notes flies through the staff like a gorgon. The scratches and clawmarks. O to have stolen those sheets and set them free, no matter how! But no matter, for the book reviews and institutions kill but sometimes serve us well. O we shall live for ever, in the schools of word-catchers as in the circles of the wise, where they talk of things both human and divine, and the museums we are prisoned and forgotten in will be toppled by barbarians, and our glimmer will appeal to one, and he will pick us up and put us in his pocket, and we will blaze anew a thousand years from now . . .

. . . with orange and gleaming teeth, next to flashes of blue sky, I chew all this inside me, and flesh it all on me with only a look, a flick, a state of blue ink shining violet, or tiny explosions on a line of black ink—behind me as I write—and silently watch the two caterpillars before me crawl upward on Charles.

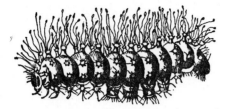

Part Three

34

CATERPILLARS
(for M. M.)

YOU SAW *all the beauty in it! Here is your nose, your bone, your lips. Your eyes are clear black. You are the Apollo of the west pediment—now black, now the negative of black—like a neon blasting your Serenity. You congeal sensation before it has a chance to break and spoil. You are waves, you are water, you are Waves which never crest or show white. You are the quiet you command. My hands are shaking.*

You are the dust of bats—seabirds crawling on the beach. You are Orange burst into black, a flock of thin wings. You are the drift and slant of pink crystals in a bottle. Blacks of your eyes to the moving, slow muscle of your arms—you are the Presider. Gold beads your hair. Blood is in your face, black smoke fades clear to reveal you, a red handprint on your back, on your shoulder, what violence have you lamb? Your white clear beauty, the slow black drift of blood in your heart, flame shadows on your chest and thighs, bits of carbon on the bridge of your nose, a whirr, a boom of gull cries, a thin stream of water pits the sand. You are pissing, you are watching the sun, Experimentalist, through a pane you dipped into candle smoke.

I buy four buttons at the local supermarket (God grant

that I could). The checker insists I put them into a paper bag myself. She says, "I can't stand to touch them, ugh. They are so cold and slimy" (sic). (Sic is for squares—perceptual idiots—who think lizards and other dry objects are slimy. I'll sic my lizard at you.) A fresh button is two inches wide and an inch and a half high. It has the general shape of a hassock or royal velvet crown—a cactus-blue top, cold and fleshy, like a huge grub or caterpillar curled up asleep, on a barky raw-umber base. It looks obscene and vaguely manufactured (prepuce of an alligator). The base is crimpled. (The amazingly shrunk portion of my father's cock behind the head. I touch it with awe. My father's cock isn't like mine, and the things he did with it are different from the things I do with mine. He pissed right into the water. I aim for the wall of the toilet bowl.) The top is divided into eight or ten sectors (the larger buttons are divided concentrically as well), and each sector or section has one or two tiny grey tufts. I pluck out the bristly grey fluff in the button's center (simply poisonous, quoth Roy), or scrape it out, the button cut in half, with my horn-handled snap-open knife. It takes me half an hour to prepare the four buttons in my fastidious housewifely way, to pluck the tufts and slice off the pale cross-sectional base bottom like a thin slice of cucumber, to pick off the rough cylindrical rind like a scab —and the soft caterpillary flesh gleaming to light everywhere, green and wet. Have I done anything so exciting since soda-jerk days when first I grilled a hamburger patty for a man who used to wink at me? Hah! Who was a chiropractor and showed me bone charts and all over them nerve lines? A tall blond boy who seemed seventeen or eighteen in a grey suit and tie, collar too big, a moustache to make him look older? He has to be a chiropractor? Yet?! Oy???! Or since first the inky dinky engine began puffing out phrases a hundred pages back? (I was only kidding—he thundered into English with grates and screeches—not no pitta patta, pitta patta—O grant they will say that about me, Lord!)

So I have eight neatly pared halves, four I put in the ice-box for David, and four I begin mincing in my Spanish olive-wood bowl, chopchopchop chopchopchop chopchopchop. Nothing to eat since breakfast and a cup of coffee for breakfast, milked and sugared, and a spot of ginger ale for lunch (my employer air-cools my outsides and ginger-ales my insides in the summer), since I want no nausea at any cost and the Indians fast and fast. Mince mince mince till the peyote is succulently wet and foamy—Roy and Allen chew it and vomit—and I refuse to be nauseated. Roy says: I can't keep it down, I can't swallow it, I'll do anything to keep from throwing it up. (Now he dries it, shreds it, and stuffs it in gelatin capsules.) Burroughs the eminent exegete says that users experience difficulty in keeping it down long enough to realize the effect. The nausea seems to be a taste problem, so here I am with a heaping teaspoonful of peyote grated like apple, one hand on a cup of ginger ale. Into my mouth, let the ginger ale seep into the bolus, gulp—washed down in a swallow—mild very faintly bitter bland planty taste. And that's that. So it's no taste problem for me (or later for David). We didn't give it time to be (our plan) or the problem accumulates with turnings-on (some kind of conditioning?) or we are hereditary non-tasters like of phenylthiocarbamide. Three more teaspoonsful and I still have a half-cup of ginger ale left. I have funny health thoughts of the green planty vitamins in the peyote, the only fresh vegetable I've eaten in a week.

Lie down, write, wander around the apartment. A half hour later: I would say that some drug effects are present, but it could be the excitement or the marijuana blasted last night. Another half hour later I am walking around the apartment nervously, feeling approximately benzedrined, waiting for something to happen. I sit down and write quietly at my desk. Shadow

OF MY PEN!

No, no, I am wrong. It is an illusion—for an instant the shadow of my pen glowed pink—my excitement—my expectations. I walk around the apartment excitedly, already glimpsing the truth, the glow, already knowing what I saw was the truth, was whatever little truth there is in my life. A pale violet corona, vibrant, all around the shadow of my head on the wall—my anticipation? The state of my nerves? Suddenly the corona disappears—no, it's not the corona which disappears, it's the sense of discovering it—no no— I can't tell—which—

I am suddenly good, I am suddenly weak, I burp, a thought of nausea, hurtling, hummm-m-m-m-m-m. I am passing through, I am passing through stars, ether blows, fins drop from my arms, metallic red sequins slowly grow up my legs, the pumping of galactic engines behind my field of vision, magnetic lines of vibration cross each other, I am a peyotaster, I shyly avoid looking at the penumbra of my shadow, I am as dextrous as Oliver, one long rubbery finger on my clock, one long finger on the pulse of my benzedrine jitters while sand pulses through my arms and legs, one long finger massaging the pile in my ass—the humming, the vibrating of my arms and legs. It is pot, it is too much, my face is hot. Click, click. Wow!

Let winds blow! Let a cape of fur fly! Let shirts come off! Let fur touch your face! Let the bright cold in!

I am travelling, travelling, travelling, travelling. Lashed. I am rocked, I soar. I am clear. I am shaking through time in cool air. I am tired and ache. I am in Death's sky convertible standing, clutching the wheel—soaked in a cool pink light while a theory of visions unfolds itself.

I am going to the visions. I will enter shaking the world of castle appearances. I will enter a Trap. I will transmigrate, it is all clear now, *I will go where they are possible.* It is a trip, a passage. The visions do not appear; you appear to *them.* You fly. The eminent exegete thinks the nausea of yage is *motion sickness. You must enter the theater, the realm.* You must get *there.* You actually must sit down and occupy a seat. It is a different *state.* The visions belong to the *state,* and you must enter the *state.* I can feel the state coming close, and yet it is farther away than you can ever imagine. I thank the Lord I can travel so fast. I am exhausted. Where is the restroom that I may freshen my face? I see the walls of my room (one yard away) through a microscope, pits and texture, but my true I hardly sees them at all, it drifts in a nebula. Nothing is left of the walls but a shell laced away and fading, a taint, a trace of ectoplasm. A skull—thin occiput plates. O I see it all now!

I am in control of myself. My eye is omega, it turns above me. My eye is luminous, bobbing in the middle of my head. My internal eye is yellow and sees everything. It is fixed, it cannot move. An eyelid bats slowly (there is no danger of interrupting the gaze). That eye is good, it is constantly shining, it glows. It draws all the vices of the body to it, it is always seeing, it never sleeps. It never pursues (nothing can fly from it). It always opens. My life, my sights lie out open before it, my white body hurtling around it through fumes, dark sea, blue rocks—as on the axle-tree of a wagon the wheel turneth. No Sorcery can change my eye though it has changed my bodies—though I am swine.

Who can understand his own book? *Naked Lunch* is not just "notes on sickness and delirium" requiring an apologetic addendum addressed to the authorities, making it clear that the author has conquered his addiction and despises it— nor it is a carnival of nothingness (Allen). It is the victory, the history of the clear eye of the mind, the eye of cold glass, of the Buddha-light—opaque and implacable, of the eye like a yellow tooth. It is the eye which Death cannot put out. It glows. It sees everything. It gathers all shame into it. It yellows. It may flicker. It shines on every page of the book; junk cannot extinguish it. (The book walks. It is Cyclops. It comes on like an F.B.I. man.)

Pangs of nausea. Little pangs—panguettes. So it is plant, not taste. I am on my divan. The thought of David coming in and my having to get up from my sublime, nauseous, zonky divan to show him mince swallow said plant nauseates me. No, no, it's not the taste, burp, it's the plant.

Gold gold God help me keep from throwing up.

THE SHEEN ON SHADOWS!

O.K. I cannot fight it. My chest is hot. Thought: Will the nausea condition me to avoid the plant as much as my mind and senses half-love it already? I am zonked. And impatient. And wish David were here. And hungry but doesn't eat. And don't know what to do (and scared). And jittering. And David shows up!

And a long nauseous battle walking up and down, talking and leaving him, to explain how he must prepare the buttons. I walk around the house in the middle of a sentence. Nausea is first. The cloudy orange sky outside is second (it is night). The windowpane is clear as if it didn't exist—that is third. Nausea is fourth. The fingers of pale green light in the sky . . . is a searchlight—that discovery is fifth. Petal light (for example the faint white glow of the cloud on my windowpane—the panes themselves are invisible)—that is six. Writing is a seventh. I have thrown myself on my bed. In a high state of excitement. Chattering. JITTERING. Nausea.

OH

GOD OH GOD I AM ARRIVING AT THAT STATE. THE MARGINS OF THIS PAGE ARE GLOWING. ALL

I CAN DO TO KEEP ON MY HEAD.

THE TOP OF THIS NOTEBOOK GLOWING.

(Throw the notebook down.   Pencil clatters to the floor.
Divan.   A pillow.)

Here is wave after wave of nausea, wave after wave after wave of honey in the blood, here is wave after wave of shadow heads, jewel glints, filigree masks which never complete forming, cold, the cold inner eye unaffected sees everything.

I am   Jittering
I am in   Pain
                        Numb
the Jittering,   Oh
my arms and
Legs   a shower of
Glimmers here in the black
              Glimmers
                        Nausea
chips of   Gold
      the huge mask of my
Jacket   Skulls
      Jittering   Cold I
can't stand it, my arms and
Legs are numb—take off my
Shoes   Skulls
Sick   glittering
Cold   peyote is
Cold,   I am sicker than
              Most   the
Eye inside   the
yellow Eye inside, I
can't Stand it
              please rub my
              Feet   the
Insects in the black

```
                    Paralyzed
    I am            Paralyzed
                    chips of
    Gold            glimmering,  I am
    Cold            Oh,                 the
                    inner Eye   the
    Axle            Jittering
    chips of        Light
    here is the
                    State the
    Blessed State        I can Cry
    I am come   Here
                         Numb
    my jacket-mask,    Oh
    Glints and    Glimmers
    my fiber      Shaking
                         I am
                    Glittering
    I am            Blessed
                         Whom
    Can I thank?
```

I have fallen, stop, and am very tired. I have not vomited but (glimmer) I am less sick. The air is dark and quiet. Steps into the city. David grows and mumbles in the next room.

That was only the beginning. My adventures in the city form a book itself—not this one. Streets and flights. Glows. Embraces. Wave after wave of hot flashes, spangles, tingling echoes. Above all skulls—not fearful. Broken sandwiches. Dead birds. Kick over a broken sandwich: chicken. Under it a dead run-over bird. It would be called a coincidence in the world I left. The flight down

8th Street with David; I was carrying a box of cookies for Professor X by its string.   The way we looked at passers-by, the way we stared down young toughs, the way lights all rushed open to us.   And then running through the crowds, with everyone's fright brushing me by.   What a terrible joy.   To each stroller who looked at me stunned I was the person he feared the most.   I was everyone's paranoid projection, the Universal Donor.

You are all the beauty in it! You are the Apostle. Your prostate is an opal. A pile in your ass is an American ruby. I wish I had Jack Kerouac's ability to quote what you say so people can see what you are—desiring this man's gift. So they can see you are nothing more than your poems, be blessed.

Professor X makes his piles seem like a bloody lobster rupturing out of his ass with a human hand in its claw. You make your little pile seem like a bubble imperfection in your crystal fiber. You have the fond feel of animals about you. You are claw, poise of skunk, pollywog. You are claw and eyes of skunk, princely stamp of skunk, meddling nose of skunk, now who knows the meaning of every preface and dedication. You are always walking into photographs. You have incredible nightly beauty.

CATERPILLARS

Look, look, master, here comes two religious caterpillars.
THE JEW OF MALTA.

I WANTED PROFESSOR X to swim through these pages like a fish—to flash here and there but to stay deep underwater. He insists on coming to the surface. He says, "I want to breathe air just like anyone else."

One day he proposed a trip to Carmel-by-the-Sea for himself, David, and me. David was to drive, and once there we were to visit the playwright Charles, a long-time resident of Carmel whom X ranks with Shakespeare. X has never said so much, but he wants to edit a folio edition of Charles's plays, and during our whole stay in Carmel he spoke of the Earl of Oxford incessantly. He was speaking of himself, and as if that was not enough, one night he said grotesquely peeling off a kidskin glove, "I myself have always believed Oxford to be the true author of Shakespeare's" (that is to say Charles's) "plays."

David went along with X's worship routine, but I refused. At the end of two days I felt my whole life had been called into question. At X's instigation, the two of them treated me alternately as if I were a stubborn boor or poor retarded child. On his side of it, Charles was equally confused. As he had very few visitors let alone pilgrims, he didn't know what

to make of the homage. He didn't know if it was real. And
if it was, he didn't know how to act. Especially he didn't
know what to make of my reserve. Sometimes he strutted
and played the role of a man accustomed to glory, and
sometimes he questioned me closely and pathetically about
why I was so quiet and noncommittal. I just wanted to be
left alone. The more I withdrew, the more nervously he
questioned me. I broke into sobs. A tear streamed down my
cheek.

And still Professor X kept pulling Charles's books from
his coat pockets, and David produced a tape recorder and
begged Charles to read his complete works. "And then,"
said Professor X, "we must show Sheeper all the quaint
places in Carmel that Charles has described in his plays,
and we must show him the house in which Charles was born,
and the stone wall Charles helped to build when he was
fourteen. And tonight Charles's wife, gone downtown to
have her sewing machine repaired, such a marvelous person
wonderful wife and mother and isn't she beautiful? has invited us to dinner. And she cooks so well."

In fact X liked the worst thing about Charles's plays—
their phony regionalism. As I slowly turned the pages of a
book, I said, "His specialty seems to be Local Color." X
said, "He was born in Carmel." "Then he must have pre-
arranged it with his parents." I felt a long speech coming
on and rose from the sofa. X was sitting in an easy chair
drinking, and I faced him full.

"Charles has no roots or natural attachment to Carmel.
Some years ago he decided to roost in order to find himself
and he chose Carmel, his birthplace. He is still here trying.
Akberg his old teacher was just as rootless as he, and used
to fly through fifteen countries a year knocking cups and
glasses off the right-hand edge of every table he sat down
to, blind in one eye. Charles sits on his ass in Carmel smok-

ing and listening to gulls. His thoughts go like this: 'Do they shriek or scream? Or moan. Do they represent America —the New World—the wide expanse of sky? What did the old padres think of them, Junípero Serra? What did Conchita Argüello think of them, playing with her pussy? The cleft in her pussy the San Joaquín Valley—the wide expanse of Spanish California her royal white ass—a string of twenty-one pimples for the missions. The space relations are all the same, her ass and the land, I see it all now, Carmel is her cherry, the sensitive spot, I must get my hands on all the old records to verify this, can I get a foundation grant?' He visits the old mission to see how the bread was baked. He sticks his head in the oven. For recreation he drives to the Château and has long serious talks about the town council with the millionaire who had that monstrosity he lives in pieced together from twelve French and Italian castles.

"I have watched you scour Carmel like a pilgrim, by yourself, hoping it would offer you the same roots and secrets you imagine it has given up to Charles. And I have seen your sour disappointed face at night. The Carmel of Charles's plays has no real substance and cannot nourish you, and how can you find in the City what does not exist in the book? You knock around Carmel like a soul risen from a body which went to bed hungry—risen to knock around the empty pots and pans in the kitchen. Thus in one sense you have not been fooled. But in another sense Charles has fooled you as he fools himself. He has sent you on the same futile chase that he's on, by bluffing you, by pretending that he writes from the Land, the Home, that he has just had mother-soup for supper.

"It's not his destiny to be the Great American Root, but that's not important, it's not his business. His business is to write plays as truthfully as he can, and to show himself and his wants as nakedly as he can. Let the heroes of his plays

bleat helplessly for a mama, not walk back and forth across
the stage posturing and expostulating, making roles for
themselves in the local history of Carmel. It's so vain. He
sets that kind of acting so high that Sheeper the Jew feels
called upon to dismiss it with a wipe of his ass. And does
dismiss it, and with it Carmel, and Charles's vanity—he is
just like a Jew trying to pass—and I have a special right to
criticize him, by virtue of my blood, of my name and bless-
ings and half-open eyes, of the candles I light, of the way
English jumped on me, a tall pale child afraid of dogs,
mother born in Europe, leaped to my lips from hers, to
which bits of thread were always attached from the sewing
she took in, jumped on me and licked my tits and armpits
and poor circumcised cock until I gasped out perfectly enun-
ciated sentences, going so far as to correct my mother, who
threw a table knife at me for my pains.

"Incidentally I belong to those things, and to David's hand,
the way it lets itself be pulled out of his pocket and held,
and to the way it presses my hand back, and to the counter-
pressure of my hand, and to the quick press of his hand and
retreat to his pocket—he is nervous now—and to the
troubled peace it brings me. I don't mind provoking you,
Professor X, in fact I wouldn't mind kissing you, it would
be like kissing snakes. Anyway my point is that roots root
among little sentimental memories like mama wiping your
ass not whole historical cities. Charlesenstein! Who wiped
your ass, was it Cunny?

"He is always coming on. He tries to pass himself off as a
man of deep thought big on ideas. His plays were written
to reveal the author as a man of stride. But they are thin
and mannered and hollow as a crab shell."

"Stop!" sniffed X. "I always thought crab-shell writing
was your ice cream."

"My ice cream but not Charles's. He writes thinly hoping

to appear thick and solid. Someone should tell him that manners—scratches of insect hands—is all we can do. That we must live in the skin where the eczema blooms. That all we can aim for is prettiness. That we take refuge from the flesh. That the flesh is unfathomable. That Charles making believe he is talking from a solid skull makes his shell echo—and the art, his art, his theatre, falls flat on its two-dimensional face. At least we can be honest and not try for Depth—it will show, it will show. Art is decorative—that's all it can be *made*. It cannot be *given* (for example) a social content. Art is Kabuki. Art is Nouveau. All art is cornflakes. Drown yourself in style—but really commit suicide—and Being takes care of itself. Art has the Being of its creator, which cannot be falsified and cannot be avoided. But it cannot be invented. You cannot write a part for it. It plays mutely, it keeps its ineffable mouth shut. Like Utaemon, with black lips.

"Charles is such a whale of a failure at pretending to be what he isn't, I don't see why he doesn't settle down to be what he is, maybe a friendly walrus or cowfish. I feel like rushing right out and giving him the long overdue lecture. But I won't. Instead, I will lay the benefit of my ardors on you, Professor X. I want to change the subject to you.

"You make the silliest statements sometimes. Once when you were drunk you told me that you believed in every portion of the Buddhist philosophy except giving up desires. I didn't know you as well as I know you now, and I was dumfounded. I found what you said so bizarre, and you had always seemed so carefully intelligent, that—very frankly—it occurred to me you were mentally ill. Later I got used to this peculiarity of yours, that when you distort a fact, you don't just chip an edge off or squeeze it a little, you transform it into the expression of your mood or prejudice. Why not be rash? For the ten years you have been Charles's champion, I believed his aesthesis too delicate for me to sense. Now I know what you moon over is the cheap Carmel flavoring Charles adds to his plays. You see Carmel through Charles's eyes because you have actually absorbed his need for roots. In his turn, he wants you to leave because he jealously sees how you dig even the cunts here. You are so fucked up in the area of possession that you covet anything anyone wants or claims he has. And you are hypergullible to everyone's claims.

"All I have to do is smile at David intimately, to pretend for an instant that we are lovers, hoping that if David doesn't refuse little smiles like that, some day he will look forward to them, that my fragile love for him will flower, the smile a root sunk deep in him, that my lover's smile will adumbrate the love to come—and yes I have pretended, in my smile, for a moment, that love *has* come—then all I have to do is smile, and you imagine a private love to exist between David and me of such intensity you cannot spend another night without having it yourself. You imagine that love to be so thrillingly young and rich (whole counterpanes soaked with semen, the fingers of love in socks, ears, hair, tongues, asses) that you have the right to pull age on it, to steal from it, to plunder it, in fact to live in its castle and eat its foods (a lamb chop with fresh tiny peas and whipped potatoes, and in the center of the potatoes a small red puddle of lamb chop juice). You are already frustrated and angry because you think the romance will withstand the unleashing of your lonely malice, that you won't get a toe-hold. And not far under the anger is your readiness to accept this romance if you cannot destroy it, to live with it, even to enjoy it slightly. Your mind almost hears David say playfully, 'Let's take Professor X to bed with us, Sheeper, he can sleep in the middle.'

"I smiled at David just as we left Salinas. You started. At first I was proud that you thought we were in love, but as we drove on I began to be frightened. I began to see the sepals of your interest curl open—the direction of your questions, your jokes. I asked you, tacitly, not to spoil things for me. I tried to tell you that I had suffered so much already, to have arrived at so feeble and unsteady a love, that I would be annulled if it came to nothing. All the way to Carmel I begged you to help me, or at least not to harm me. I begged you to pretend, with me, that David was my lover, to treat us like lovers. I promised that if you did that, by an arcane force I have some access to, by virtue of my blood, I would give you—in the form of David or myself or any thin boy or flabby lordly man of age and cock—the lover you have always wanted. I don't know how much of all this I succeeded in communicating to you. I think as soon as I indicated how helpless I was, you pounced. You saw through my eyes the love I pretended, and so naturally you decided to have an affair with David. I gave him up without a fight. Even before we reached Carmel. And you were ill-tempered rather than grateful or victorious, because I had retreated before your maw could mutilate my neck, cracking bones, or tear open my thigh to the iridescent bone.

"Don't you think of an ever after? Don't you think of having to see me again? Especially when you and David have a fight, in a day or two, or a week if you control yourself—and you'll call me on the phone and invite me to dinner? What will you say to me across the table as I rub my finger sadly on the edge of a plate? Will you ignore completely your destruction of my love for David (thin alas, but my hands were full of love)? You are the Destroyer of Love. You are the Destroyer of Parsimony, because the idea that you can love is Lie Lie Lie, and you brought my love to waste for nothing, you have nothing to replace it. And you set your self-interest above mine, viper. Aaaarghh, I am bleating, Sheeper.

"I think of how sweet to me and appreciative David was every time I introduced him to you or to Y or Z. I loved it. He wanted the prestige of associating with my friends, and I gave him the opportunity to meet them all, and he was grateful to me, and I enjoyed his delight. Sometimes it was not so honest. Sometimes he saw me or arranged to see me, or said something to me, or did something for me in order to meet someone through me. Do you remember the night after I introduced him to you—ah and how wonderful he was to me for that introduction—when you invited him to dinner, and he insisted on your inviting me too? He wanted me along to be a buffer between you and him, and for no other reason. But I let myself be used, because I use other people, there's no great harm in it, and I loved him besides. There are elements of payment and barter in all kind accords. I respect those elements and give them their due (I have a nose for business). Tomorrow or the next day, when I will tell David that I cannot see him any more at all, in order to protect myself, my Self, I will at the same time, in an angry silent stage-aside, upbraid him for a short count, that is, for having decided not to give me in the privilege of his exclusive company—now he would be seeing you whether he saw me a lot or not—a fair return for the many introductions I had given him. I will be giving him silent notice of the severance of our commercial relations, now that I am taking a loss, and all this going on under the counter, so to speak, alongside the other, the talk about love. . . .

"Business is business."

Part Four

36

HANDS

SOMETIMES MY MOTHER punished me by ordering me to bed. She would lie on the bed with me, and then crawl under the covers. She would tell me how bad I was, and how I let her down. I was old enough to understand her hard life, she said, I was old enough to realize how worthless my father was. She admonished me never to follow in his footsteps. Then she would pinch my ear in mock punishment, saying "This is mama's naughty ear." She would pinch my eyebrow, and then my cheek, and then my nose, and then my throat, and then one nipple and the other, and then the skin around my navel, and finally my penis. "This is mama's little tootsie." She paid the most attention to this part of my body, and on the next trip around she would omit an ear or a cheek, till finally she was jacking me off, and I knew it. Suddenly her mouth was on my navel, and I can remember trying to push her head away, my hands in her black springing brilliantined hair.

These are not my hands in front of me, no. These hands are covered with dry spots of eczema, and my hands are long and sun tanned. This mind thinks of things like how to mask the sound of pissing, and in my mind pissing doesn't exist. This man taps calamine lotion on the scales of his forehead to ease the pruritus, and my skin is glassy and warm. This man's cock hardly comes up to the perpendicular, and I, well you can guess I am only sixteen. This ass sucks up knives and forks off the table. I take sun baths on clouds. This man has never hooked a lover, while other homos live together. My hands close reflexly with each blow of pleasure, and I am blown as much as I want.

My hand is always warm and trembly, and I daresay a bit moist from where I always have to pull it out afore I can shake hands with a gent or lady, who may have wanted to meet me in the first place because they caught me with an arm in my Levis up to the elbow. But I never want to meet *them,* moist as they seem; for letting another person into your body secrets is poison. The source of human misery is intimate relations. Snap them. O pop the blowsy promises of love as full of air as fuchsias. God gave us separate bodies to lead separate lives with—let us keep to ourselves, live by ourselves, and see others when we run out of incense. God gave us, in our own bodies, all the tools we need to satisfy ourselves, why not use them?

What lover ever came through when you needed him most? Stick to your fingers.

37

VINEGAR AND ITS WILLIES

MARIAN'S REAL LIVE LOVER of course doesn't show, so she and I make LSD . . . starting with daisy petals on the floor and little burps of pleasure. Cometh pale pink and then giant fingertips double and duplicate everywhere, tending to fill the room and flicker, like in an old movie. Then glints are a swarm of bonafide metallic beetles, mirror-green and yellow. *Get back into your cracks, barks, and crannies, ye great chartreuse host!* The air is so thick with them it's amazing we get through it as easily as we do. Now some of the little beetles have turned emerald blue and some are magenta and some are dull whitish turquoise crackled with black. My fingernails are green and orange. Bars of dark and light play over the page, and have you ever tried to write by the fucking Northern Lights, with a thousand insects crawling on your hands besides? Sparks and aces are flying off the page in every direction. From each pen pressure comes a spray of brilliantly violet diamonds. We bask in Egyptian sunshine.

I look at Marian and as always see four or five: a shy awkward young dike, a snuggly kitten, a dark seductive Carpathian beauty, a fashion model posing, a pleasant middle-aged Jewess coughing up a lox bone. Seeing her aggrieved of her lover, I am grown so sad that writing it my right arm melts off sympathetically. Is she a thief? Has she stolen the writing right out of my notebook? All I know is that certain passages disappear completely. Can the book itself know how much I hate its narrow margins and erases my best passages in spite? I am paralyzed with doubts. The drums say worry! worry! and every fact I know appears in a halo of is it true? is it true? O I cannot be L.S.D. Sheeper, that is too powerful a name for me—that I must have seen on an envelope addressed to someone else—whom I respect and even fear—the papers that name has signed, the deeds done. Why am I quaking? I believe that no one eats but me. I was damned to live among the squirming human worms who thrive on love and sunlight, and to humiliate myself, a grosser thing, by eating. They egg me on by pretending everyone has to eat to stay alive. They make me see an old man boiling rice on a hot plate. They rattle chain after chain of supermarkets.

Tastes fill my throat. Tiny red and green starpoints pass into my mouth, and can be tasted! They are biting like soda water. My tongue and fingertips are numb with electrical shock. And cold. Ice crystals seem to be forming in my hands and mouth. I am very cold internally, and nippled and trembling with cold. Rubbing hands does no good at all. My muscles are excited to the point of spasm. I am convulsing and scared. Extreme physical discomfort. A bad high. A Time Magazine drug. My fingers are locked in grimaces.

Hairs keep growing in my mouth, and sand forms at my fingertips. Such fingertip buzzings. Light pulsing or quaking across the page—waves of cold quaking light. I keep wanting to shriek or let a hundred squeaks inside me scream all at once. My muscular discomfort takes on the colors red and green. A paper-thin ebony arabesque forms flat across the room. Two thin sectors, and a third, appear in the air and then fan out into three whirling mosaic discs. Stone columns start whirling and twist into spirals like taffy. My mouth is autonomously alive, and seed pearls are forming under my tongue. Suddenly my nose, which has been running steadily, dries up. I launch a long self-analysis in the form of a lecture to Marian:

"There are times we must give our minds over to friends who are each other's enemies—to be used as arenas for battles which we must not enter. We lease our minds out like stadiums, so to speak. And other times an individual will file a claim of eminent domain, and we hand over our minds without arguing. What paws! What pachyderms! What honking giraffes! What prehistoric newt or giant sphenodon! What hulking sloth with dragging hands! A muscle moving in the damp black back. The monstrous limb and wing are crushed in the mud. You somehow have to lend these types your mind to live in or they perish. You have to let them roam around in it, breathe deeply, and clutter it up or do as they wish. Your body is completely useless to them, they won't even make it with you! They say hurtingly, 'But I never thought of you as a body.' But that body is up all day and all night holding up that head the mind they occupy is in, but they don't think of that, they see your body dangling uselessly from your mind like the arms of gonionemus pulled up from the sea. They see your mind as an empty box to fill with their genius. You are indispensable to them. In your mind they shine like a diamond."

38

FINGERS

HE LEFT YOU CRYING in a cold water flat—crying and rubbing the scars of the ass warts he had given you six months before. ("I must have caught them from a girl in Kerista—sorry about that.")

He left you in a flat full of furniture crying for daddy, and a tear swirling mascara streamed down your cheek, which you pressed to the glass door he had painted black to keep his probation officer from seeing you waiting in bed to love up your man after the horrible monthly visit. On that day nothing but cock in his body could make him full, and no matter how down your cock was or passive you felt, you were glad to fuck him—and to keep it in without coming as long as you could, to make him feel good.

So you tried to paste the pieces of your broken life together, so many slivers missing in cruel, illogical places, and you lived in his spaces and filled up his drawers with your things.

And a year went by. And then one day you saw an old friend talking to a boy in a jacket red like your lover's. You wondered who it was, but your friend looked pained, so you walked on. The same afternoon you passed the pair of them again. Your friend's face was frozen, and you looked hard into the eyes of the boy in the red jacket. It was someone you

had never seen before. Your eyes dropped to a rip in his
jacket—that you yourself had sewn up.

Now your eyes dipped into all the bony angles of his face
and skull, the cheek, the hollow of the eye, the back of the
head. It was not the old familiar terrain, far from it. But your
heart stretched its wings till they tore, and you recognized
an ear you used to nibble, and a nostril flare. And then with
sudden sadness you realized how wild the untended bones
of your loved one had grown in his absence.

Anatomists may bristle tough and white as the bone they
write about, but all go soft and wax about how *plastic* living bone is. Take heed, you who live with a lover, to protect
his looks by kisses and molding his face with your fingers
whenever you can, otherwise the bones may as in the sad
case recounted grow chicken beaks and beetle horns.

You might think that when love was done in, the writing
would sputter, but no, we go on, we keep chewing the entrails including the horn, bone, and nails. To keep dicing the
tripe. Ah not to love love enough to be blasted dry, but the
pen and the mind do not falter.

Not only not falter but they catch feelings like flies and
suck out their juices. For example I recently met the author
of a book of love lyrics, poems written after the love was
done in, they are psalms almost. They are tender, hushed
with love for the lost lover, and look backwards with a sad,
exquisite vulnerability. There is not a single defense or justification in the whole book. I told the Poet how surprised
I had been by the total absence of bitterness in the poems
and by his refusal to question the love affair in any way—
to regret it or belittle it. He spoke of his lover quite openly
to me, and as he spoke his voice grew hoarse. The man he
described was stupid, unfaithful, selfish. Intermixed with his

—I must call it hatred—were flashes of love of the quality he had captured in his verse. He closed the discussion of his love affair abruptly, with a cynical smile. "At least I got a book out of it."

The Poet fights with his fingers. I do so many things that it looks as if I were an outgoing person always experimenting. When the fact is each activity had to be learned in spite of myself and against my nature, under conditions of fear and shock. I want to learn nothing and live in my innermost core—as far in as I can go—and would drop all my outside accomplishments for a drop of love to touch me there. The Sheeper in my face is what I touch when I seem to be playing with my beard. I am like a man with an ass filled with figs, who has climbed up a fig tree to eat them. A fig picker catches me eating what he thinks are his crop and beats me. Look at the poor aging and now crying queen being beaten. All she wants in life is camp, make-up, and a few of her own figs.

I tell you they may love you as much as they can, but it's never enough. Stick to your fingers!

And if after masturbating you have to get dressed quick and shove a detumescing cock safely back into buttoned pants, don't be surprised if it leaks a little. And be proud of those stiff stains on your underwear, they prove you're a man, and semen isn't a poison to be wiped or washed off skin, clothes, or bedding, but an Attar of Narcissus lingering on in the bed for days. And if semen glues your penis lips together, and piss comes out in several streams or an uncontrollable spray, unstick those lips by pushing your piss out as hard as you can. And a good asshole finger-fuck is fun but first moisten your fingers with spit.

Do the great American forests invite the country boy to

lie down on pine needles under a tree and jack off? No, they are impassive. They do not invite him and do not reproach him afterwards.

Orange light on leaves. The smell of tea. Blue light on leaves. Our grocery of leaves. Aspens hash up the light, and the pine tree kisses and powderpuffs us. Its arms are pine. Its hands and face and cock are pine. Its pus is pine. I am a shudderer. O Dirigible of Beauty! O Dust! O Stoops of the Forest!

39

PICKING LEAVES

W E VISITED THE CHÂTEAU, David, X and I, before we left Carmel. A giant's fairy castle bathed in colored lights, and the bathroom walls studded with Roman tombstones. Green light on fronds, flowers, and a green pool out through a fireplace. Between the sixth and seventh windows up of a stone circular staircase whose rough walls floated like mist, under the gridded pale blue light of an iron lantern . . . my soul began to leak. I shut my eyes to fight it back in.

Thought of the kidskin glove X stole at the Château three days ago. Does the millionaire suspect him? Thought of the key the brown ghost to whom I appealed for help and who ignored me stole. Brilliant ideas or talking through space to the absolute bottom. MY SOUL LEAKS OUT AT GO SIGNS.

Or can leak out like gasoline, the jelly I'm filled with, but want to conserve it. Shut my eyes . . .

. . . to angels crowned in alcoves like medieval princes— the doorway of a bakery at midnight, it's a little windy, I can spot him looking sullen five blocks away, leaning on his right shoulder and left leg, the right leg bent, hands like arrows in jacket, collar turned up, crotch stuck out, stop stop stop while I tell the world how sick I felt as I walked upstairs holding tightly my key. For I moved my eyes from his, not the reverse, while my inner eye stays glued to his brown eyes and black curly hair. Repeat: jacket collar turned up, the right leg bent, desert boots and white wool socks. I am now going to jack off and show the world I can make it with him anyway, and the pull of a shirt on my back is his embraces.

If I don't go to Heaven, and if Heaven isn't lined with all the sixteen-year-old boys who even go so far as to make the approach to me, asking me where to catch the D train for a meet with his girlfriend on West Fourth Street—he is late—and I asked him if he plucked his eyebrows they were so straight, which he didn't raise to answer no—I repeat if those boys don't give me a second chance to pick up on them in Heaven where I won't get off the D train in a panic bumbling, but with God's help I will ride all the way to West Fourth Street, where there never was a girlfriend, even I knew that when he said it, and "Gee I guess she got tired of waiting," and I am supposed to say, "We're not far from my pad, care to come up for a beer?" I say if this doesn't happen in Heaven then I have wasted my life.

Why do we have to pick leaves (kiss) or search among the branches instead of taking hold of the root itself?

We have to be content with the evanescence of pure Beauty and not try to capture it in our hands (the scales will come off) nor, worse, try to capture the artist in a butterfly net. If I were to show you some of the letters and poems addressed to me by the Poet, you would say, "Here is your lover. Snatch him forever." But I know the Poet nags to death the people he loves; no one can live with him; he is worse than a woman. Only in the poem is he tender, breath-

lessly so. His writing is the perfection of his love and longing, which he feels but in rare gleams or flashes, in the life
he and I, and all the rest of us, lead together. And so in this
life likely we will be always apart, though in Paradise we
will walk arm in arm.

Why do we have to pick leaves (kiss) or search among
the branches instead of taking hold of the root itself?

I'll try to answer but I don't really want to. That is I don't
want to tell you about two boys, fourteen or fifteen, lying in
the sun on the pavement, the first warm day of spring, oblivious to the mixed reactions of the passers-by. The head of
one is in the crotch of the other, they are both wearing Keds.

I do not want to tell you about them because I do not
think I can handle it. My notebook is a tangle of arrows
and scratches. The margins are crammed. And what I had to
describe is so simple, that I'll try to tell it to you offhand,
maybe this stratagem will get it said for me.

One of the boys, the one whose crotch is being used as a
pillow by the other, looks enough like Piglin to be his
brother. Perhaps it is Piglin himself. If so, it is Piglin at a
point of such radiant beauty in his youth, inside and outside,
that it could only have lasted a few hours, perhaps this one
afternoon. Suddenly Piglin is brushing his friend's hair vig-
orously, as if to sweep off the dandruff. Piglin's roughness
doesn't at all conceal the extreme tenderness of his action.
Now my own crotch is tight. Then Piglin took his friend's
hand and held it crudely. My heart pounds in my throat.
Because any gesture more than a look or thought conks me,
seeing two boys smile at each other I already see them
smelling each other's armpits or asses, my cock throbs, my
balls shift, I am ready to ejaculate, with not even a word
spoken, no wonder I can only hint at things, I go to pieces.
To have *sex* with someone, to bring cocks together, or cock

into cunt, is an act so extreme how can anyone tolerate it? It is stimulation of peyote intensity without peyote means to handle it (and peyote fills me with the fear of dying and the courage to die). Fucking forces me to place myself in the strain of shock, of anaesthesia, and what a horror it is to make it with someone who grows more and more excited, who will not be muted, who will fuck you, who will pour stimulation into you, who will never think of how much you can handle (unh *anh* unh *anh* BABY BABY BABY BABY, as X said to me, his denture clicking, and then demean himself to apologize for coming off, I'm sorry *anh,* but *anh,* I'm *anh* COMING, my God I thought men his age never come I must be pretty sexy in his eyes). Numb and ashamed I let them have their release but never come near me again.

To tell you the truth, a glimpse of Piglin was all I could stand, under normal conditions, without anaesthetizing myself, and tired old queens like Professor X are going to find this memoir boring because nothing ever happens, there is no love-making, there are no culminations. To return to the sidewalk, Piglin's hand-holding was shy as well as tender (holding with only three fingers). This is Piglin, Apollo of the Skin, at this one moment in his life when he is tender and vulnerable, is it any wonder that my hand has wandered into my pocket?

Hand in hand the two boys lay motionless, perhaps for a minute. Suddenly the other boy sat up. What unspeakable turbulence of the crotch or heart does each feel as he sits apart, breathing rapidly, each recovering his composure, there on the sidewalk, legs akimbo, both pairs of Keds are new, I'm almost certain Piglin has an erection, he looks at a passer-by too boldly, both boys exploring old houses together . . . the smell of clay . . . wet leaves. . . .

My cock is soft and droopy.

THE ETERNAL RETURN

AND YET WE ALWAYS tend to carry intimacies into the sexual realm, where the more potent emotions can be employed to cope with them. The sexual realm or rupture, seam or juncture, more often gap between people, at least if one of the people is me.

Sex often gives a person his only glow, and what are you supposed to do in the half minute after orgasm when all the glow is gone? The orgasm is a pearl engulfed by two lumps of oyster meat. But the glow of love shall span that breach and the glue of love shall stick my and my lover's bellies together.

Use the Sheeper Test to determine whether you are queer for somebody's soul or just got the hots for his body. If you just got the hots for his body, don't make it with him if you want to forestall that half minute after orgasm when the only bridge between two people has been blasted away, and you lie in a lonely annihilation, embarrassed and naked, being rubbed or fucked by a piece of wood, and you couldn't care less only wanting him to stop hurting you, and when will it end, and how did you get into this in the first place. The Test is to jack off with the sexpot in mind and see how you like him right after you come.

It is the responsibility of all fuckers to get up where your beloved thinks he is. To fuck that as a target. And just as the smiling Japanese fucks seven women at once, a half dozen dildoes spaced on a bamboo crossbar strapped to his hips, likewise you should fuck your Mexican's weird intelligence and grace of dark skin turning darker where it bunches in the small of his back as he leans back to pull up a white wool sock and mental beauty of his long animal vacancies or two-day silence because speech is worthless until you get frightened and yell at him and then he talks to reassure you and beauty of nervous gesture, his gentle hand on your arm or head, and himself he gives you the candy bars he eats himself and all his candors. To hit his sacred places. That lean brown body pushing upward in an empty bed. I rush to his side.

The job ahead is to hit it. Dead leaves. Floods of heart attacks. Fleas. Hit it! Hit it! Appetite and diseases! Hit it! Fringes of flaking skin. Hit it! The gigantic cock of a tiny redheaded fairy, thank God you are fucking *him* in the ass. Hit it! Hit it! The wands of the snail wave thee back and back. Here is David's carved jade or ivory: "I used to hit those dumb Italian kids, I wouldn't think of coming on to any intelligent boy or even Jewish, I would be too embarrassed, I had this routine, I said, 'I guess you got a lot of girl friends huh, you ever lay em?' They always say yes, I said, 'Can you do everything to em, they ever suck you?' And if they said yes, I said, 'You ever get sucked by a fellow?' and so on I mean to hit the Mama Lode you got to go through a lot of shit." Hit it, you hear? Hit love in the mouth. This red fez Egyptian selling the sailors aphrodisiac paste in a little tin box spots the merchant queen and whispers if I fuckee I tell my compatriot co-workers, who will remember you on the next trip through, and though you may grow old in the Merchant Marine you can always count on being laid in the

Suez Canal. Hit it, hit all those spermy glands and canals inside me, fuck me, I got a cunt and manly arms. The drab of carrots and sardines, tin after tin after tin after tin after tin, desert sand on deck, the sunny grey days, ankh in wet scarab sheets, the same shipmates, the same tensions, the same cock under the pants, cock under the shorts, this ship you blow one, the next trip you get another boy hot, and don't think it isn't a struggle, you have to maneuver an army of Japanese postcards, and blue novels I have to read out loud yet so many early maturers (yummy) leave school for the sea, and inventing sexual stories from my past to order, whatever the quirk unkinks that pink, not to say battalions of innuendoes and actual gropes—I'm a fucking five star general. And they write long homosexual sagas in England leaving out all the juicy parts and wanting me to say how courageous they are when all I want to see is slippery slimy cocks in print. Hit it! Hit it! Paste newspapers up!

41

MEXICAN

I LOVED WHITE SKIN for being white and brown skin for
being brown and Mexican, here my white love and brown
love eat each other up like cannibals. David's skin is white,
and I loved David more than he did me, and I loved the
Mexican more than he did me, but I think differently now
as Time shrinks my vanity. For David loved me as much
as he could if slightly, he knocked on my door almost every
day, I had no bell, and I lived with the Mexican for a year,
and he always came to my bed to kiss me goodnight on the
forehead, even after his "dates"—and what right had I to
be jealous of those sweet girls or of the hustler for whom
David occasionally broke an appointment with me? Here
is a letter from Kinky.

Dear Sheeper:
   Out with Roy's Wife recently. What a surprise to see her
fat. Says you have key to her pad, as we will be staying
there when we get to the city. Cool cool baby that's me,
like hot ice! Loved your photo in Loot. Quote, how sweet
that is, Sally. She sends love and jazz. We staying in David's
pad. Sally mad as hell, says he kept her up all night making
it with some cat from England. Slurp slurp got boring as
hell. I was out at the time so missed fun. See you soon.
                                                    Kinky

What am I? that I don't see love when it loves me or beauty which lit me up. What right had I to be jealous? I was gifted with love. David, did you love me and I not know it?

Now sex is an itch that should be scratched, and a prick should be masturbated in a cunt or mouth. But love is something else. "What silly romanticism. Love is a quantity, just an itch to be scratched, with more ghostly fingers but just as mechanically." These considerations will drive me to slink out behind the old icebox, my mind in my mouth like a piece of raw liver and gobble it up.

And sometimes wisdom seeped from his brains like white come oozing from his dark skin. In my memory I kiss the Mexican again, his chest, his nipples, never his lips which he always refused me though I saw traces of lipstick on them plenty of times. Once I complained. I said, "You kiss girls on the mouth but not me." He rapped my head hard with his knuckles and said, "Look to the ways I love you." I drew his Mexican eye in the air when I was alone.

His fingers were brown every time I looked at them, their half-moons white. Every time I saw his skin I fell in love with him all over—mouse skin—the glossy brown fur. I saw again the white come on his dark belly in the morning. He was nude except for his medallion but I wouldn't take my yellow shirt off. His cock was even browner than his body. Or flooded with red in the glossy black hair. Ah flashlight of come on my tongue!

I found your cock searching for my asshole, trying too high, trying too low. You found it, your hand guiding your prick, and I was terrified. I love you and let it go in. I sweated it in. And love wasn't a sweet of the heart alone, and it hurt me. The mechanics, the fact of them, hurt me more than the fucking. You were gentle, you asked several times if you were hurting me, not too much I sighed, but you didn't take your prick out, you shoved him in deeper, gently, to give us more pleasure. Where did you learn so much younger than me?

And much later, after I had stopped attending my afternoon classes in order to give my body a chance to cope with his cock, or mouth a chance to blow him more feelingly, and a month of afternoons had gone by cock to cock and body to body or cock in ass as I held his waist for dear life, I would suddenly show up at an afternoon class in order to take a test. A ray of sunlight in the room would take on his odor. A sign like this of the Good Powers turns my fragile flesh to diamonds.

I had shoved a graduated series of test tubes into my asshole, over about a week, to widen it enough to take his cock without discomfort. I finally succeeded, in the sweet name of Love.

He too unlocked a door for me, to his room every afternoon when I came back from class. He had left it unlatched, and I would knock once and open it softly. The room was filled with sunlight and he would wake from his nap just enough to raise the covers with one arm and beckon me, impatiently, with his hand. I threw my books down on his desk and ran to snuggle in the smell and warmth of his body. We lay together for an hour before getting up for dinner. What girl of his ever got more?

His hairline was too low. His nose was too thick. His ass was too lean. Otherwise his body was as perfect as a sentence, and I used to mutter those flaws to myself like a breviary, so as not to be paralyzed by his splendor.

One day another student opened the Mexican's door without knocking and caught us curled in a chair with opened-up clothes. The intruder turned back in embarrassment. I worried for a week that we were going to be expelled. I kept waiting for a summons to the Dean's office. But the Mexican laughed at my worry and treated the whole matter with the nonchalance that comes from doing something true. He knew we were Protected.

He always laughed when my eyes touched his face. To have given someone this delight, how did I do it?

And oh shock of delight when I first realized my touch or presence was enough to give you a hard-on! You kept that fact concealed from me for weeks, and I was too innocent to see it. All I could see for weeks, was that every day, just when I yearned for you the most, and grew mute with feeling, you stood up abruptly with your hands in your pockets and left me. It always happened when our spirits were most in rapport, when my heart was laid bare, and I took it for a cruel profound punishment I must have somehow earned. Then its meaning, and your own bashfulness, dawned on me like suns. And so I looked forward to the moment your hands sought your pockets, and I forgave you your shyness, and let you slip away for weeks. And in my first notebook I wrote: "His hands slipped into his pockets. My 206 bones smiled in their sockets."

I woke every day for a year with the same terror as always—but then when I woke up more I remembered I would spend that day with you, and the terror fell off me for another morning. A whole year, and still I woke—and still I wake—in terror.

And who can believe he is loved till ten years later? A memory comes down on me fast and hard, like the Mexican the one time he blew me, his eyes red. His black hair stood up in stiff clumps and straws, with three Indian feathers at the whorl. My palm was on his ear and fingers on his scalp damp with sweat and Kreml. Ah the peace he gave me. He loved me enough to violate his own nature, and is this the only measure of love which will satisfy me for a moment? We are all trade queens stalking the Mexican boys who will put us down. To seek love where it cannot exist and was not offered, to think of a proof of it, he is blowing me. And that I was given this proof I wear on my finger now I am older like an invisible ring which I touch at least once every day.

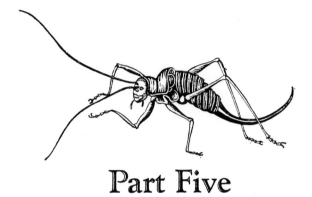

Part Five

42

STYLE

PROSE STYLE is a fistful of marbles dropped by a king's hand onto a billiard table. His fingers are covered with rings. Picked up and dropped, picked up and dropped, while he is waiting for some important state event or ceremony to take place.

Style is the grimace or face we make waiting for the painful pimple lance—the strain which drowns out the pain and makes the deliverance possible.

Style be my wall that nothing breach you till it burn from inside me. Tower over the light little flames, let them die out too hard to write, that only the flames hot as the cock I hold out to my readers—big but very gentle and loves to be snuggled—ignite you.

And the high wall or weir that style is makes it possible to say what would otherwise consume us. And then, only then, can we smash the stone prose releasing the clamp of style a bit for the hot come to ooze in filling the chinks.

The world of art is made up of poses. The pose is the fact. Think of all the camp queens everyone judges to be what they are posing. See Dietrich's female glitter as the masquerade it is in *The Devil is a Woman*. Compare the irritability of Proust with the grace and charm of Marcel. The honest pose is part of the truth—not a lie. The best part of Proust is what he wanted Marcel to be. Fat black doctors have an unerring sense of their high points, and they flush the rest down the toilet of mortality. Reading a book of poems we see such stars in the Poet's mind we toss the book away, run to him and hold him dear. What we find in our arms is a yowling child or monster, but who has, if we look hard, a pale glow of beauty he must have had to tap and distil for years to make stars. Digging everything I say about poses will help you see underneath everything skin, to the few bones we really are. We are high queens in the ermine of poses. The fingers which broach our cape are studded with rings.

First the high points—an eyeball, an earring—then everything else is suffused with light. The platinum hair. Even when the screen is black you can tell where Dietrich is standing.

It is more than a halo effect. In your brain a tongue forms that can taste the sweetness no matter how highly diluted. To this curious tongue a page obscure becomes a pool of honey from which streams of flavor swirl. And then you see each phrase or sentence tapping its foot impatiently to give out its meaning. Finally your insatiable tongue demands the writer in flesh if he is alive. "Pull down your pants," the tongue commands. Meanings creep.

With your glutted tongue back in its socket you sit back and dig the meaning wreathe and flow through successive sentences like the streams of birds—first one stream appears and vanishes and then two or three others—and each bright racing flock lights a short brilliant part of the long winding route through a book.

Granted that a writer wants to love up his readers and give them something quite close to sperm. He is too shy to reveal himself to them in person like a Christ or Buddha, so his love and beauty have to undergo mechanical processes a thousand times more terrible than the act of love—have you ever seen a printing press running or a folding machine? By a mysterious law of conservation, allied to the true grace of the Word, his love and beauty pour forth from the freshly printed book unaltered and oh! sweet for all time. In olden days they wrote on stone. We write on paper in a stone prose, for the love to last. Our lives are lived in miracles, who can doubt them?

Have you been touched by a book whose author still is living? Love him back. Seek him out and help him get over his shyness. Love from the past can kindle our spirits like gold and rubies set a thousand years ago, but live skin yearns for the touch of skin.

The feelings books contain are real. Books should be covered in skin if anyone doubts me. Books make mistakes just like people, for example by using vulgar words for very personal or unique emotions. But when you have convinced your readers that at least you aimed well and are not trying to eat up their senses with bullshit and meaningless repetitious propaganda, then you can use any word you want no matter how wide its currency because they will believe your usage and prick up their ears even to "gruesome," "cock," or "Eisenhower."

An ambiguous sentence (or word) can store up meaning. In this case some following sentence not only clears up the ambiguity but illuminates, by its own clearness added to the clarification it carries. But a vague sentence discovered must be recast. Vagueness of mind should be shown exactly, through the windowpane of the sentence, which must always be clean and clear.

You have to go after a sentence spitting teeth. It would be content just to float in a muddy pool like a medusa. You must seize it (beware of the nettles) and shake it. Shake it out like a sheet, till it falls smooth, again, and again, and again. Weak talk.

The sentence must be clanked. You have to start with a sentence and clank it. You have to plate it with metal. You have to galvanize it. You have to coat it with small iron links and give it a bath in acid. You have to screw it till just before it snaps—let it snap or shatter. You have to cast it in bronze or fit it with scales. You have to hammer it out thin. Then out with the tin snips, boys, and the blowtorch. Solder or weld it as the case may be. The sentence must be *transmuted*. It will be *metal*.

I can give you a museum of examples, an empire of accumulations, accretions, a sample of golden lodes. In areas that have nothing to do with poetry and prose. Gold. Cobalt and bone. My palm bones were electroplated (clanked). Dem golden bones. There, that's it, the example I want, Kink-No-More called "conk" for short, raw is, kick me no mo, suck ma cock instead (the voice of a spade tickler, black moths and blue brass trumpets). Do you see what happened? Addressed to high white society.

The sentence must behave. As soon as possible for the longer you work on it the more brittle it gets and you may have to detemper it. And then set the sentence in plaster. Meanwhile you crank up the paragraph, sometimes the motor catches two or three lines from the end, sometimes it doesn't catch at all. Let the paragraph knit like bone. (Meanwhile you fold in the cocks—honey, homogenize that prose.

It's your job as a writer to prepare a text that is unbowdlerizable.)

The connections in *Naked Lunch* are internal, forced by the voltage. You don't see the connection, you don't see the connection, is that a brown spot in the middle of a sentence —turning black? Do I see smoke?—the crackle of paper— a dazzling blue-white bar.

See plot for what it is, read *The Unfortunate Traveller,* and the rest of the sanctified conventions—conventions simply to hold the prose together become ends. Use any kind of glue or real paste, for everything stands or falls on the closed inner circuit, on the circulation of Light in the writer, on a fixed pole of Light in the flight of phenomena, relax and enjoy the scenery, the Odessa Massacre in *Potemkin,* everything will fall into place. Don't tell me you don't know which way to look at the clouds. Let your hands Fall, let your ass rot out.

All this is Ancient History to poets, and any prose writer who has ever been exposed to an Eisenstein montage and still hacks out Story ought to be hacked into the bits of hamburger I am supposed to sprinkle on the fruit salad I feed my lizard. For cinema is prose. This is so obvious that the new crop of French realists called "objectivists" who copy all their techniques from the movies (without saying so though they have said a lot about their new way of writing) are dated and boring. Prose is cinema, prose is cinema, prose is cinema, the Light of this discovery has long since been shed, now press Light from there.†

† Scientists (writers) throughout the world: Choose your facts (images) and let THEM speak. Choose them with your HANDS. Keep your mouth shut, like Utaemon. This is one of the few places where I ever talk.—*Ed.*

Words glow because of the underlay of sex. Cloisonné glows because of the underlay of silver and gold. My Indian silk gossamer glows because of the faint, faint underlay of brilliant eosin. Do you remember when fuchsia colors were chic? I believe ladies wore turbans. The sex in the words is real, not literary. The bulge in the book and the pants is the same. All there is between a reader's cock and me if I am still alive is the mechanics of bookmaking. If the book or word were to disappear, you would find out how real the sex is because you would be pushing my head away, you can't stand so much pleasure. And would you understand if I plunged my hand right through this notebook into time, process, and distance so that it emerged out of the very printed page you are reading and reached down to grope you? I bet you have a hard-on right now as big as mine. Do you want me to feel of it (cocktalk of Melvin Sanders)? Do you like this book enough to press it to your crotch or breast? Kiss me.

Need we go through the whirls of personality just to reach cock? A resounding no. Just reach right out and grab it on the Williamsburgh Bridge, unattached to any psyche or particular set of clothes, free-floating and unattached to any body. No one has the right to lay his person on you as codicil to cock—that's blackmail. Always grope out and short-circuit the coy meander. Reach right through the page with your hand. Pay no mind to the maze of colors, just grab. My cock is throbbing for you. This prose is a new space I built special for an eager hand to plunge through. Put forth your hand.

I am trying to tell you that certain sentiments, certain de-sires are so strong they exist outside of vehicles, outside of books and human bodies. They glimmer through centuries.

You look for Baudelaire's secret. You try to find his treasure hid in the poem. You wonder what about him shines like a sea-shrimp through the history of poetry, indeed through his own book. It glimmers in the black sea. It may vanish for an instant, but here it is again. It is cold and bright. The words are the magic themselves and are black and white. They shine! There are no secrets but the poem! They are all here! The poem is opaque as a mirror.

In olden days they wrote with ear and eye. We write with our fingers always reading what we wrote like Braille. And one minute I'm one inch high down on the handwriting it-self like a mad jabbering Chinaman jumping from one live wire to another, screaming at the words to behave, pulling an "and" out sideways, kicking an "m" in the ass. The next minute I'm back on stage bowing low—in rhinestones—in the richness of robes. The fingers which broach my great collar are covered with rings. I move slowly in the long folds of prose.

How to X-ray an ember. Blow on it. How to make the sun blink at you. Look at the sun and it will blink at you. How to make a stove come to life. Light the oven and roaches start crawling. Steal a peyote plant and it will scream "Jewels!" How to make a word glow. Trade secret.

Things glow because of the underlay of ownership. (Those last-stand defenders of capitalism who may construe this remark to bolster their cause, open your eyes. You should see tomb. This book is not addressed to you and pre-supposes the passage of a century or two since your deaths.) An old newspaper clipping about the shortage of high school teachers in Brooklyn is the most valuable object I own. It has knocked around so many drawers it is soft,

brown, and brittle, yet each time I come across it when looking for something else, I move it aside reverently not to
damage it further.

How many people keep things in drawers, and if so what?
And do your drawers fight with one another for spheres of
influence, one drawer insisting that she alone can store
thumb tacks, but a few rebels always finding their way into
another drawer?

To make things precious by keeping them. By putting
them away and never using them. The good dishes or eau-
de-Cologne. As opposed to schnooks who buy a favorite shirt
and wear it out in a week. Not wearing the shirt that
makes my heart thump, and wearing the shirt I like least,
often, gives my three-shirt wardrobe a range of value bureaus
full of laundered shirts do not possess.

To make things precious by using them. The image used
again and again in different contexts doesn't pall, as we were
taught in school, but pulls strength into the line. The line
or routine David uses on little boys to get in their pants has
been polished and perfected by so many years of use on so
many different subjects, it is as pure and delicately simple as
carved jade or ivory.

43

DRUGS

To lie around like a lizard. To be diamond grey. Heroin is the first night in this new season, lighting bulls and darts and the blights. The fine inchworm writes, "Love is better than books." Into the vein. Is junk love because love hunger vanishes? My veins are sore. I still have a foreskin and am standing belly out at the mirror. What a long foreskin. To still have a foreskin some dark lover would always think of when he thought of me, his secret office thought. Let him quit that office job already and drive piles.

Crossfire of salvarsan. Secrets of cloth. Elbow, poise of shark, twitch of tail or ear. Blades of steel and tail fins. Shark light. A whirl of propellers. The silver verses slice each other. Iron tingle, the tines of a fork. A crust of smoke or fanny smell. But, or, film, or—navy peach. I wanted the powder. What a combo, Sally and X. Candle jam. That pile of ice cubes Acropolis. Gutter of book. Tears or eye squirts of blood. Money flows in my veins again.

I am richer than kings. I own crowns of umbrella tips. Oh my gold brains in the shadow of combs! Out of the marvel of this green wall see a riddle of spikes. Gold flies walking on paper. God of the ringing bells.

Great white canopies of drugs overhead. When will cocaine come into my life again? When will I smoke my next joint? All these questions hover like great clouds in a certain area of my mind overhead.

To swerve stars. From each man to pull his sweet song. To put a star in the reader's eyes. To shine a ray right out from the page showing him himself and how eloquent he is for being that. To be his Magic Mirror. Is it love or cleverness that knits the lines together?

Alcohol is the excreta of the offensive, repulsive yeast germ. These germs live and swim in their own offal, till in wine the filth becomes so dense that they literally commit suicide—poison themselves to death.

Cocaine is the startle of sunshine on a turbulent sea. Streams of light reach from the heart to numb the teeth. I am forever in debt to my donor as I patiently coax a wad of love to shoot up in the sky like a rocket. To thank the sun with a plumspray of stars. Let all dark brown hair, damp and heavy, for a moment turn blond.

Now everyone is acting. Everything is props. The world is engaged in a gigantic benign conspiracy to force you to be what you are. Every night all the people you will speak to on the morrow hold a secret, informal rehearsal. Beer is served, and David laughs with the grocer.

Pot is THEATER. Everything is bathed in stage lights. You yourself are an actor, if you muff a line so what. All situations are scenes, all places are sets. All objects are props. They squirm, how can you take them seriously? One thing turns into another, a clock peels. This world is floating. Objects parody their former selves. A shoe comes on like a substance. "I'm all *shoe*," it warbles, shuffling along on the floor.

The eyes and clocks of light all over this apartment—not a timepiece in sight—but hemispheres and globes of golden light.

O worlds that I dream loose bars over—globes of orange light—command me to stop hating myself. Command Jonas to release the one part of his body that calls to me through his clothes and frightened monologues. He is always afraid and erect. In fact his prick has been so hard so long, it has grown a fingernail. He is afraid the soul has a bourn or bottom, and if someone fell in him, deep, they would be trapped there forever, in the dim inside light of a vase. Wine-colored drapes torn and faded. Piles of old clothes. Old motors and twisted airplane parts covered with grease. Corrugated boxes, moldy and water-stained. He is afraid they would lift the flaps of a box and find it filled with dirty boxer shorts, stained and some even caked with shit. He would laugh nervously and say, "Haven't had a chance to get to the laundry this week."

A glass scarab falling down a stream of candlelight. A part of Irving is constantly giggling. The moth crawling on the ground in circles, beating its wings. The train passes over rail rifts. Or objects sprout tiny dove wings. A thimble levitates and flies across the room. Grasshoppers have jewel eyes. How come I won't let my own jism rest on my belly but am wiping it off? Worlds change with the bat of an eyelid—let the words tumble and letters break apart like sticks.

Pot has affected me permanently. I'll be looking out the bus window: A street full of people, but a scene. The play has fallen into scenes. Does everyone know what a scene is? A scene, a set, a surface, a flat canvas painted, and to prove it the figures start squirming (slightly). And around their peeling edges you can see the glassy jewel colors of other sets and even the (!) shining grey space between scenes (the screen). All sets have lost the hooking dimension, the real dimension, that makes you think you are hopelessly stuck with them. And it was hopeless, till teatime.

Or you see a candleflame more truly as a hole in the dull grey wall of your room, a tear in the shabby fabric of the world you kiss goodbye, knowing that behind that fabric is a world of orange light, which leaks in through the flame, touching your spirit, telling it there is a finer world, infernal, more brilliant and swirling, where men fly like eagles through the radiant smoke, or pause drifting upward in the empty space, talons outstretched in the air, long golden necks craning, bright orange light-gleams on feathers. How patiently that window-flame wavers!

Pot is EXAMINATION. To watch my pen write these words. To see the very form and essence of my own handwriting as I have studied it with sly and wonder from time to time form on the page like a genie. The ball point opens up the line, and my meaning develops a blank page like a photograph—already shot eons ago. My hand is like a whole old ugly spinster scooting across the dining-room floor, hunched and pulling a black shawl tightly around her shoulders. This handwriting which is the surest thing about me—that half the wonder of writing is to see the old unchangeable pattern revealed—that I am grateful to have something so unquestionably mine—that I am I—that this pattern is lashed to the fingers as they twist over, writing. I hate those white fingers for letting themselves be used. They are revolting and meek. I look in the sky sadly when nobody comes to visit me for weeks. I see my handwriting there and silently admire it.

Pot is rancid POTATO CHIPS. Dark bitter juicy potato chips are too well done for me, I prefer the crisp sweet kind with patches of white. Especially if they're big, unbroken and salty. Roy's Wife is the mistress of potato chips. Watch how she holds them.

Each time Roy got high he would laugh "I'm going to

the store to get me a candy bar. Anyone else want one?" He would put on his shades and go. He would return later with a little brown bag, give each person his candy bar from it, and then, last, he would pull out a bag of potato chips, which he would open noisily and pretend to gobble up greedily. Then he would laugh and pass them around—a bonus over and above the Milky Way or Peanut Cup each of us was eating.

Roy's Wife adds hot sauce to her india ink and sprinkles paprika on the still-wet drawing. I give society marijuana treatments like a fat black doctor. Into myself. I am Gifted (poisoned by light).

The pleasure of drugs is gratuitous. It is not a wage, desert, or reward. You should smoke tea because it's a gas, and you destroy a valuable principle, you make drugs a commodity, when you give them to yourself because you have done something admirable.

William Rattrap has to take an expensive drug he asks for a pencil to write out the name of—N-benzylphenopropionamide—which is addicting but the only drug that holds his brain disease in check. Finally out of exhaustion, pity, and impatience you grant him his little addiction. "O.K. O.K. O.K. you are a bonafide dope fiend—here is your membership card—and inveterate bore." Then he asks if you would care to join him in a reefer. What 1920 dictionary of underworld slang has he been reading in bed? What he brings out looks bought pre-rolled and probably filled with oregano. He lights it and hands it to you in a studied hip way. After one drag the blood chimes in your head like a bell. You look at him incredulously. He is gazing downward, toking his joint like a pro, a true teahead coming on like a square for inscrutable reasons.

Tea keeps my mind from strangling itself in red tape. It

shears off the doubts and qualifications. It pushes uncertainties off the edge of the cliff. It lets what I feel stand, so that I am simple and sure. It gives us our second chance at love and sex, all drugs do. Think of the good spirits or angels that I can never touch—in boys' faces. Think of the hundreds of boys I do not look at for fear of looking at them with desire and its endless complications. But when I am stoned, collar turned up and wearing my shades, I plug my mental cock into one boy on the street after another.

Desire—both ways—is good for people. It makes them shine. Have you ever seen a group of hip boys on the subway giggle and chatter when they sense a man flashing eyes at them? Have you ever noticed the strange, easy, beautiful way teaheads enter each other's worlds? Tea makes them blossom or tower.

Under tea people are drained of their richness, their poverty is blessed, they become the few bones of what they really are.

And so what do I care for all the facts I forget, the phone numbers, rare earths, where the tea is stashed. (And anyway where *can* an ounce of tea be stashed? for anywhere your mind can ferret out, they can ferret out too. Go draw something ugly.) Tea has rinsed out my brains, which could never give up a fact. My desk is strewn with papers which I now keep face down. And when my lizard climbs out of his box to shit on the desk and soils a collection of papers, I throw them all out without looking—and never miss one, these papers that cluttered my life.

Tea kills the sense of loss that makes us less than perfect —the sense of duty or charity we feel when we give things away or do good on principle. Streams of warm tea mix with the ice water that wells up in our breasts as the price we pay for giving our guest the larger morsel of chocolate cake—the cold price our bodies shiver to pay for the pleasure we set out like General Booth to give others. Tea kills that sense of cost or sacrifice. It makes us the diapering mothers, dreamless of Florida.

When you smoke pot your time is pulled out like taffy. Roy, his Wife and I are stretched out on a bed, and the last band of the last record has played. Who will turn the stack over? Roy is looking at his Wife, she is looking at the wall, and I am trying hard to look like a guest—let them fight it out as usual so I don't have to interrupt my escalator trains of thought and lizard peace and make my way across the room. But they are holding out, they are not moving, they would prefer silence to the onerous job. Already Roy knows what I'm thinking and is about to say "Why don't you turn the records over Sheeper?" and Roy's Wife will add "Yeah, you're the host," the two against Sheeper as a walled city sinking, and so I undercut them and struggle up from the sea, and waddle across the floor shaking out water, palm over palm on the wall, my long thumbnails tapping, and stand before the Victrola, the record still spinning, and slowly push my hands into the awful machine—when the next band, the real last band, begins.

Pot starts the escalators, and the trouble is, the one trouble with pot is that language suddenly falls beneath your ability to utilize it as rapidly and precisely as your thoughts form and drop off already fossilized sabre-tooth turds.

There is such a thing as drug paranoia, in which you attribute all your pleasures and appreciations to the drug rather than to the poem or painting. You believe that nothing inheres, but the drug gives it life. When you shoplift a book or a pound of coffee, you say it is Drug which has done the thrilling, infamous deed. You think of the lifted portion of your library as the Drug Bequest. You suddenly realize that your drug friends are the only friends you have —is human love nothing more than getting high together? —the real friends (my God I think it's true!)—and then lie in languor and wonder why it was given you so to delve into everyone's head and genius including your own.

Nothing exhilarates me more than to make good connections. To transfer onto buses the drivers are ten minutes late already. In my saddle, to throw an arm out the window and suck a back hand.

I dream of fluids thinner than water, a pinwheel, spring, or feathery spray of perfume.

I feel so bright and happy! I have a negative headache! The wind blows through the windows! The air is quiet, nightly, and cool! Here is a cup of coffee! I wish all quiet libraries were open at this hour! These secrets of happiness, to whom can I break them?

For all the poets alive when I am alive, for mayonnaise and marijuana, for the Light that shines bright and clear (when it shines, which is rare—powers, please note), Whom can I thank?

Marijuana heightens all our sensibilities and makes us more sexy, but without causing us to cough up blood or waste away. (In fact, Jewish mamas, it gives us an appetite.) Whom can I thank?

Marijuana has taken the place of consumption. And
Peter is lying home like a skull. And
The flames are in me, a nervous smile
To the lunatic smiling on the seat beside me.
I put on my shades
To watch him masturbate. Pretty soon
He tickles my hand.
Whom can I thank?

O potent drug that has hooked me like nothing else but boys! Brought me to New York! Showed me the meaning of five or six pens scattered under a ream of paper! Told me that *that* is what life is made of, those facts or states suddenly made true! Looking for a pair of socks in the morning! The ugly red rubber balls a dog chews! Red rubber balls roll into my prose! O spew of pens! Become lilies! Given me the involuted intelligence to see the very fact I am talking about, hidden till now like the pens! To exult in the pens under paper! That they are there! That no one but a sheep has ever written them into prose! That everyone else has ignored them or similar facts! That I might have ignored them, but Drug made them to live! Shown them to be there! Turned iron-grey into silver! That the pen I write with is one of those pens! Its tip is brass!

44

STONE

TAKE STONE as a subject, like "Brian is stoned." He is only sixteen. The two stones in his scrotum are swollen with milk and cry out to everyone Brian smokes with to give them relief. They twist and tug at the gauze in his white fairy cock to make it curl straight up like smoke in a fold of his thin blue pants.

As an aphid shedding sweet drops of honey dew at the same time feeding on leaves, I got no time to waste, I gotta skyrocket ant fortunes. So what am I doing with this pen and scraps of paper? I walk into a delicatessen and order a boiled ham sandwich like a good Hitler youth. I want an air hammer. The proprietor slices the ham. I want a cement company or steel mills. There is a tattoo on his forearm—a six-figure number. I am a faggot or man-eating burglar—and this is the shyest of ovine memoirs.

See me play the association fibers of my brain like a harp or throw myself into states of parasympathetic vibration and not always able to smash the stone prose. Or even if I can smash it I wanna be a poet because it's too embarrassing packing around an air hammer and a piece of pavement, my dear. I wanna flit around in a grasshopper topcoat and tiny goatee, licking fairy cocks.

But what I am is the King of Clubs brooding—with leaden rings on all my fingers but the stones are real.

45

SKIN

SKIN AS A SUBJECT. The dry twisted foreskin of Jesus at Chartres was brought to Charlemagne by an angel. It looks like a flake of Archangel agar. Orange-skin on the rosewood table, or web of the word Moroccan. A stake of fingers. Flowered drops. Long fingers yearn for a ring or a beautiful strap to carry.

My skin flakes off in leaves. A gust of David come blow them away. Give me the strength to kill flies and fill out income tax forms. Take me out of my shingles. Cactus flames, brain flames, the smoke becomes flames. People we frighten are the cocks of our eye. Think of Apollo's cheek power. A finger creeps up to my lips and pushes them open.

Chevaliers! Let blue touch your faces! Hear the pung of steel kisses on squares of peacock feathers! Sharpen the orange blades! Slaughter the bird! Command the kisses of Franco the black parrot! Say: I want your steel kisses O camerad! Franco you pace the Alcazar, girlish hands behind your back. Your flat sad arrogant face. The long green finger—the pearly claw—a parrot feather—drops to the floor.

LAW OF THE TALON

I have something all over my wrists. Scratches. The claws of my iguana are sharp.

193

He hates me
        bites me
Blood flows.
I clip his nails the very tips, too roughly.
Drops of blood form red like mine. The same amount.

For an hour, an afternoon, it is possible with expensive soaps, ointments, and mechanical measures, special strokes and massages, perhaps not to arrest the flaking of the skin, but to conceal it, so that for an hour, after a day of applications and awkward positions, it is possible to achieve the semblance of a clear smooth skin, that love may go its course, if it will, which is not likely.

Do I have to give any more lectures on Piglin? Is David far behind? I wonder what he's like, what his cock looks like, already ask him to strip except for his fishnet shirt.

Pulling off a kind of clinging skin or web. Other days having to be pulled off of things yourself.

Pull the skin off my mind. Step into it like Yopi Our Lord the Flayer, two hands at each wrist, his own and his skin's, his *nahual* (disguise) the *tlauhquéchal* (spoonbird) (not the *peyotl*, caterpillar)—all this is Nahuatl. The moving parts, the helping parts, there where we help ourselves, our arms, our legs, our eyes. Our thin parts moving, the skin on our temples. The hanging parts, the flesh on our backs, our bellies, tender, thick, it becomes tender, stains, stains things. "His cult is one of those most repugnant to our sensibilities." He was the god of spring. The gong.

Skin as a subject. David brush the leaves away (dandruff). My skin needs the saliva treatment and so how can people sell themselves or live off their skin? Hands are black soldiers. A brown bottle of clothes bleach—I will never escape from my skin. I keep wanting to launder it like lace. Will peyote starch it, stretch it out thin? More people than David place me in a category which they then, since I am silent, stretch to include themselves. What am I supposed to do, have an argument with David about semantics? I don't mind a harmless or comic gentility, and he is metal pounded out thin. I open my mouth and tiny blue explosions come out. They sting my mouth. Thin electrical noises from my windpipe. Mechanical lice running all over me. Fat flies, thin rings, asleep on my belly. I am afraid of contracting the eczema in which the skin becomes gilded. Bits of skin loosen themselves and stray about me in a ring. I positively astronomize. A swarm of beetles and botflies in my telescope. The lenses wrinkled. The mind spoiled, rumbled over with seeds, papers, fearing. Doilies cut from tracing paper make a weird currency.

Art as skin. Lizards are all skin—no hair or feathers for lice and fleas to cling to. Completely non-allergenic and very slightly affectionate (when cold they dig the warmth of your hands). One BM per week and odorless. The ideal pet.

The skin of my furniture as my own. So that if you X sit on my toilet I can feel your weight though you are skin and bones, and if you Kinky tear off a few splinters from the edge of a grease-stained table by trying to open a coke bottle on it I will conk you on the head. My chairs and tables are broken, the paint is chipped off, the floor is covered by dust, but under the dust the skin is taut and unbroken. All my table tops are backs. All objects are alive. I step softly.

46

AIR

TO HANDLE ALL OBJECTS as if they were alive. To live our lives out of objects. To cherish them. The hand curved around the stone or cheek. (Can you trust yourself to the hands of a man who wills bread crumbs on the floors of his château [tenement]? His fingers are like sticks.) To fold our towels and face cloths. To treasure furniture that it will never be left broken in the street. To reverence the dust or bread crumbs which lie on our floors. To walk lightly so as not to disturb them—to respect all debris. (To be torn between respect for the floor and respect for the dust—ah let's leave this interplanetary battle in the cold ether.) To respect all objects as if the people were gone, perhaps killed by ether or streams of radiation, as if you walked in an abandoned city and knew there were only yourself and the objects you saw. To walk on wood floors and then sidewalks, the treasured areas. The city is a sanctuary. To behold the ice cubes Acropolis once before I die.

47

RUBIES AND DIAMONDS

WHATEVER IS PRECIOUS, the rose sachet or nesselrode, whatever is folded, whatever is wrapped in moleskin or chamois, whatever we keep to ourselves or nibble secretly, the note found in a bone china teapot six months after the funeral: "This tea set is for my granddaughter Marian, with love from Grandma Ashkenazi," whatever we show our friends with a sinking feeling, knowing how amazed they will be and then sad it isn't theirs, whatever notes-at-the-door that long ago should have been thrown away but our hand was stayed graze like sheep on the top of our bureaus, whatever a mighty hand has trapped a flame in, whatever we give thanks for even though we may not know to Whom, whatever someone cared for back in 1910, whatever is wrought, whatever is swept, whatever is salvaged from oceans of chaos, a little money saved at the bank, maybe a sweet showered body in prison and maybe the soft smell of sweat on old ladies, whatever we take extra pains for, whatever we make carbons of or transfer from notebook to notebook, whatever we pull the cloth over or off of, standing back like junkies to watch flashes take place in other eyes, whatever we earn or reap or bring back alive, whatever we strip down to bare essentials or gild, paint or remove paint from, whatever lips we brush a crumb off or tiny backs we scrub, whatever we lock up or set free, whatever our eyes wander back to, whatever we talk to in our palms, whatever we lie back for, whatever shines like a damselfly's body even though it may be human thoughts or acts or the way a huge young hand barely rests on its owner's knee—that hand is so passive and gentle, whatever we take to bed with us, sexpot or vegetable, or mineral rings that glow in the dark, whatever wornout slippers our mothers had to steal from under our beds in the dead of night to discard, replacing them with hard shiny new ones we cried and went barefoot rather than wear, whatever sweet perversions we will not be brainwashed or bamboozled out of, and lunatic prejudices, and people we dislike innately even though they may be wives and lovers of our closest friends, whatever suddenly becomes clear, whatever changes before our very eyes, whatever makes us whole and clear even though it may be anger, whatever slovenliness or massive disarray is used to hide a mind in perfect Inner order, whatever we apply iodine to, whatever takes fire from a match we applied, whatever hidden eloquence comes gushing forth from mussed-up hair, whatever sends out streams of light from white wool socks and moccasins, whether it is the man that put them on or the brown feet inside them and perhaps appendages have their own inner light, whatever gene or genes it is that makes the big toe of some people shorter than the second toe and thus gives to that big toe, normally gross and swollen, a certain grace.

OBJECTS

TO HAVE OBJECTS all around me in my house. To know exactly their state and location in that incredible disorder. If I do not see a brass soap dish for a month, I always add the right amount of tarnish to my mental picture of it. A list of Chicago phone numbers five years old, even though nothing but death is left at Chicago, where a great Christian god spits teeth at Pak. The wax candle with ends melted over I shove up my ass when it longs for a cock. A packet of all my letters of introduction tied with a heliotrope ribbon— letters to unfrocked priests, letters to Socialist poets scrambling all over each other to be the first in their countries to employ the latest decadent techniques, letters to expatriate Englishmen, quondam advisers to sultans and pashas and long since out of favor, but who represent themselves pathetically to tourists as the power behind the throne, letters to a Cuban refugee poodle barber, letters to a Chassidic rabbi who wears out a kaftan a week, so many devils rub against him, letters to the descendants of the lawyers who handled Beethoven's thousand paranoid lawsuits, letters to ineffectual professors who come on as great campus favorites because of their unorthodox clothing or mannerisms, but who, when the chips are down, betray any cause or student at a frown from any vested authority, though their tenures are unassailable—every school has one, a math professor who thinks himself the flame of the century because he comes on like Will Rogers with an Oklahoma drawl and treats elegant mathematical concepts with the most corny insouciance: "Dx is a little bitty piece of x." . . . "Infinity is a long way off."

A thousand details spring up like Myrmidons, fierce, rosy, still in their teens, greaved, bucklered, and ready to fight for their lives. How the quality of debris left on a plate changes with time, bits of tuna turn dark and become hard at the edges though they stay plump inside. If the hot water doesn't run tonight, will I patiently wait for it or rush to the window screaming "Turn on the hot water you bastards, I'm in the middle of giving my baby a bath"?

Can the cold acid jolt of orange juice in the morning make you angry? Can you hear a thick overcoat falling to the floor? Did you hear the soft tap of its buttons? Can you recognize the clinkety drop of a pencil—to an inaccessible place? Did you say, "Go annoy someone else, Objects, ye impertinent servants"? Do you calculate how fast or slow to let out a fart, taking into account the location of your friends, the prevailing winds, and the volume of the fart pocket—that is, is it a big fart pushing out so fast the only way you can control it is to swallow it again, or is it a tiny fart that has to be strained and strained out and then it goes peck instead of orbleboorp? Are you a believer in burial without embalming? Do you believe in the natural deterioration of little notes you carry in your pockets—to the extent of putting them back in your pocket if they fall out when you pull out a handkerchief, knowing which pocket each note belongs in, never changing notes from pocket to pocket, watching them grow soft and wrinkled but not discarding them until the words thereon have faded completely away?

To see OUTSIDE yourself. To come upon new oil-fields of interest in studying your life, and to flame them out. To go outside and look in the window. I am weird beyond redemption.

To stand OUTSIDE the things you do every day—not to be aloof from them! never!—but let them relax and take on their natures. The act of looking for a pair of socks in the morning is smiling. All ordinary things see you look at them newly, and they glow and relax in your interest, and drop all their cares. The last oily crumbs in the corner of a bag of potato chips invite you to eat them all up. Things tempt you and play with you again, as when you were a child. The faucet handle says, "See how thin you can make my needle of water before it breaks into drops."

To stand OUTSIDE the things we pass every day. O marvelous bakeries! The glistenings and glazes! The way lemon custard fillings steal into our hearts! Big brown crumbly cookies! O all initial wonders fall on us like flowers!

To be too weak to kill a cold so wall it up. To live *around* it, so that everyone can see it in negative only, by the cough drops you take. Kiss you turn down. And so we snuggle under the covers only to think of setting the alarm clock.

Electrical noises, sine waves, embarrassed static. Mama, fix the TV.

That the red stones of my ruby ring gleamed with green and gave light blue and orange flashes. That's why I wear it, it's like a handful of jewels.

49

THE OLD AND THE NEW

THE OBJECTS OF OUR LOVE and hate change frequently, or periodically, or never, but are unstable, while the modes and ratios of our inner lives remain fixed. You who have known suffering will always know it. If your grooming had to be perfect when you were five years old, in order for your presence to be grudgingly acknowledged by a father who wouldn't speak to you if a lock of hair tumbled onto your forehead, then you may live like a sloth in such personal disorder it has to be smelled to be believed, but your sentences will shine like skin.

The fact that we have hatred levels to maintain doesn't make a concrete peeve or hate any less authentic. The world is big enough to fill up our quota with objects well worth hating. Nor question your fears. If you are afraid of everything, the simple reason is that all the things you come across hurt you. You seek them out, but that's immaterial.

If we live we must eat. And deal with others to get what they give out. And so we cannot indulge personal rancors too openly. But we can divert them by brains to the good use of Art. Let hate go up into the flames of beauty. Or encrust it with beauty and the hated one will clasp it to his bosom heedless. Every artist hopes the world will fall for his shit and keep his turds in a glass case like amethyst geodes. For whole cities to swoon—and they know not why—in the high perfume of a fart!

We become art fiends who deem everything that doesn't leave a residue of beauty sinful. We know David blows boys with his heart and soul, and yet we think it may be wrong. In theory we know anything done wholly if it does not hurt people is good. But old prejudices and new fanaticisms make us hesitate. We look for a justification, however slight. We urge David to write, to turn his transactions to the good use of Art.

50

AN ARMY OF FAT BLACK DOCTORS

JACK SMITH SAYS, "It's good for an artist to fall in love with the mediocre. How I adore Maria Montez with her stunning 1935 padded shoulders, that marvelous creature, that sheer gossamer goddess, I have seen the *Cobra Woman* twelve times in my life. All during my childhood she was my ideal of raging pasty glamour, and all I want my photographs to do is recapture what she exuded."

I am not sure how much it profit an artist to fall in love with the mediocre, but surely the images laid down in our childhoods are the *mises en scène* of our lives, and trivial infantile pleasures and shynesses the great windy powers we summon to art. My mother was a tiny chattering woman who could bully no one but an infant. Alas I was her infant and now blast trumpet and tuba against the monstrous regiment of women.

I am not sure I know the meaning of mediocre, but surely the fat black doctors pant so hard to bring beauty to light that they will take the moldiest subjects—believe me—and make them shine—the wartier the better. We look for beauty in the least likely places, as much to exercise our beautifying power, clearing our nose so we can snuff air up into our brains, as to send a work of art soaring through space like a planet, with the same incredible impetus always that we gave it to rise from such ugliness. Art is all about toads.

Beauty is always haunted by ugliness, and the more hunted down the better, and that is why fat black doctors are not too careful about removing chisel marks. They want you to keep in mind what they started with.

When Ulysses pinned down Proteus, that Old Man wiggled according to his nature. No matter how enchained we are, banned or inhibited, everyone has a tiny margin of freedom to display his nature in. This is no excuse to make men slaves, but good fat black doctors elude enslavement by magic. They take their tiny margin and make a world of it. The whole screen is taken over, limits in another world of discourse, and all their senses are drenched in freedom.

Every fat black doctor has to build a texture his imagination can live on like a slug—rough like sandpaper or so soft it cannot be felt, like bat fur. And each man has to give his life a texture rough enough to include everything he loves to do. I like a good comic texture, when a man tries to sell you something in a good-humored way, both of you knowing he is only trying to keep alive, how can you put him down.

And every fat black doctor has to learn to put his purity where it belongs, in his profession, and not to start sculpting his life, which is after all a mere palette, as it were, for his art. Let the life go to pot. Let the body grow as corrupt and bourgeois as as it wants. Let the eyes grow sentimentally wet when you're flattered no matter how falsely. It will cost your art dear, in the long run, to place the shadow of a check on your appetites, foul and selfish though they may seem. All a fat black doctor can ask of his life is to let him forget it while he is dreaming. It is simply a matter of putting things in proper perspective: one pure line can set a thousand births at rest.

Fat black doctor keeps giving objects eyeshine treatments

while exposing them to the world gradually. "Seems to be working all right," he mutters, "a little too early to tell. Here, give it another dozen megavolts, make it fifteen. Jolt it with eyeshine and show, jolt it with eyeshine and show, this is my whole philosophy as an electrical engineer and Magician."

Fat black doctor gives a course in Beauty Trap Detection, and I am on a gurney with a towel over my ass. Fluorescent liquids fall and rise in glass gauges, and we are flanked by racks of test tubes and hypodermic needles. He bends over me smiling, holding an electrical instrument behind his back. I can hear crackles and see curls of smoke rise. "I am a fat black doctor," he roars, and rips off my mazuza. The towel slides from my buttocks. A thick wiggling finger suddenly jabs up into my ass as far as it can. In spite of the shock and pain I get an immediate hard-on. The doctor is saying, "We need a sample you know, so just shoot off and enjoy it. Note your cock has been placed in a mason jar. The jar is embedded in three kilos of surgical cotton . . . just in case . . . you really let go." Now the doctor addresses the medical students standing around me:

"And all this is for one purpose. To see if the patient has startracks in his blood, urine, or seminal fluid, as is shown by comprehensive examination or case history, even though they may be from the jewels in a wrist watch, or a few chips of crystal scattered in the words, pale trace of a ghostly gleam remembered he wouldn't tell anyone except a fat black doctor clever as you must be.

"Magnification is no problem," continues the fat doctor, wheezing. "Gentlemen, if we can detect a millionth foot-candle of starshine, we have found the star. Magnification is no problem. And it is a simple technique we can impart to the patient in minutes, like giving himself a shot of insulin. But naturally there has to be something to magnify, there has to be a trace of starlight no matter how dim, in a word, gesture, or garment the patient wears close to his skin. To be metaphysical, ahem, if we find an opalescent treponema in some lushed-up paretic's blood, we can mount that precious jewel in a ring such that people will never lift their eyes from his thumb to his broken-out face. In short, beauty can be found, revealed, and dramatized, but not invented.

"Stop! No need to invent! Images are already cast in the mind of a Beauty Trap. Take down every word he says.

"As to the question of whether or not beauty exists in everyone, in various degrees of hiding, leave it moot. Lovers of humanity will say that it does so exist, and I will not argue with them. For me, as a fat black doctor, it all boils down to how much work I am willing to put into the examination before I get a positive finding. When I am exhausted, I give up and write negative. That does not mean no beauty present, merely no beauty found. Another doctor, more clever or indefatigable, or possessing a more sensitive set of esthetoscopes, may come to a different conclusion with the same subject. In my mind negative cases are always in some sense still before the court.

"There is such a thing as the opposite of beauty—like positive electrons—a peculiar turn of mind in a patient such that all the preliminary findings point to a star, but the conclusive determination shows not only no star, but a dead black space which silently swallows up any star which may drift across it. I consider such individuals to be true aesthetic perverts, and I treat them like pariahs. We have enough trouble panning for stars in the gloomy Yang-tze of every-day life, without having our stars thefted in the night by these unfathomable characters, whose thirst for beauty is so unquenchable they can pour down their gorges an ocean of stars and writhe on the sand for a century, parching for some budding Gertrude Stein or Melville to annihilate."

51

T. REX

MARC PUTTING DOWN Cuban men for being bad lovers, that is, for coming off in ten seconds and turning over and going to sleep reminds me of a passage somewhere—my book is like a half re-constructed dinosaur skeleton I am sitting quietly writing inside of—where I put down anything but instantaneous orgasms as being clod-like. Speak of justifying our own physiology.

Finishing this book is like trying to get dough off your hands with a marshmallow stuck on each finger. Is there a door? Did you ever dream of making your way out of a room filled with mad strips of paper whirling when the sweet vanilla batter hit the fan?

I am like a king stamping through a room filled with furs —stamping and trying them on.

THE SUBLIME SCENE

To go home and write the great scene. (And I shall step home like the African queen. Or trudge to Cathay, pushing one fur boot ahead of the other, lost in my own mischief.) Or stay here at Malka's writing it all night.

"How exasperating can you get?" I screamed at the Poet. "A full minute I have to wait before you interrupt your trains of thought to answer me. Now, what are you thinking about?"

"The Emperor and his wife," he answered softly. "Was there ever an Empress Josephine?"

The Poet's middle name was Joseph. Perhaps a specific event in the reign of Emperor Joseph had plunged him into this particular trance. The same vulgar preoccupation with royalty. Where did it come from? (As an aristocrat and snob of the first water, I recognize no establishment of any kind, but make my own judgments, and go through life awarding peerages and indeed am surrounded by princes. . . . And why am I so careful? Why are my mouse judgments so certain? Because as a Jewish Negro homosexual I cannot afford to be wrong. I am a doctor of making up my mind. I take pills without water, chew aspirin and swallow jewels.)

Suddenly he spoke: "I was wondering if Emperor Joseph had any connection with my grandparents."

I shuddered with embarrassment at so shabby a delusion of grandeur, which was also sad because in his domain the Poet himself was the King acclaimed. He smiled sadly in his reverie. I said, mocking him gently, "What makes you think your family is connected to royalty?"

He said, "I see jewels."

I said, "Your family is horrid—they drove you mad and now want to clap you into the looney bin. Whatever beauty you see in the world was placed there by your own hands."

"Or by those of the dead," he insisted. Then he pointed to his forefinger just above the knuckle. "A ring will appear. From where else could it come?"

53

SEAMS

O R SEAMS AS A SUBJECT. In the seam everything changes, at the interface, all our strengths and weaknesses live in seams, all the world is in seams, not in dreams, do we see anything, all else is ground. My soul is the summation of change rates at seams, $\sum \frac{dy}{dx}$. The seam in the eyefield at night is the go sign, and at the go sign soul leaks form, you can't help yourself, like in a dream, and think of the gasoline in airplanes, a bullet comes tearing through the tank, and it heals, and what jelly does my soul contain? A string of go signs down Sutter Street is a row of bullet holes in my breast. I force myself to look away or I am dead.

The seam between a man's soul and the world is always very interesting, to see what kind of makeshift gate or subterranean labyrinth or time-lock doors a mouse couldn't squeak through, he puts up. His relationship to that sodden world *is* the purity of his art or spirit drifting upward in the empty space. Our dove is always haunted. The prose is so ugly we cannot release it, but in our flight, in our running hard and panting, a wind carries pages away.

All body strains are in the seam or septum. The harelip. Piles in the ass where the gut meets the skin. The eroticism of ass and cock and mouth. The simplest stitch is enough to make men lascivious, therefore Christ wore a seamless robe: I say this on the authority of Akberg the eminent Old and New Testament priapologist.

Genitals are so rubbery and unconnected with the rest of the body—like ears—that if you love a body you love back and thighs and ass, and loving cock and balls is extra. At first they are spigotted leak holes. At puberty they dissociate from the body and grow flabby and pendulous as the body grows tight and angular. The purpose of pubic hairs is to hide the hideous seam. Never explore anything covered with hair.

(Ass on the other hand is an integral part of a young boy's anatomy, and when you dig a boy—his soul I mean—what is more natural than digging his ass? What better expresses the soul of a boy than a warm whiff of shit as your cheek rests on a buttock? Young Sheeper dug ass. As natural and harmonious as the love of ass is, certain practical problems are raised. What can you do to an ass if you do not wish to banish it to the nether regions, where of course a small hole in the middle of it can be fucked? What can you do to it face to ass, bluntly speaking, especially if you're the kind to brush your teeth at night? A young fellow is not overly fastidious about wiping himself. A cock can be lipped and tongued, and fingered very intricately if it's the kind that sends out pre-ejaculations, samples of come, Nature's erratic provision for queer sex [not all cocks leak first, and some of the campiest queens I ever met turned out to have cocks drier than the mouth of Paul Bowles caught between Taroudant and Tafraout with plenty of keif and no water]. Compare with cunt, than which there is nothing wetter in my experience, the danger being death by drowning. Ah me, the answer is to lick shit.)

David is so ashamed of his line or routine for coming on

to boys that I have never got it out of him entire—just in a few words here and there I have had to fit together. He is ashamed because it is patently phony, but I worship it and want it down for two reasons. The first is that it is a thing of beauty, worn smooth and essential by years of use and possessing the simple intensity of a carved stone or seal. The second is that it is an opening, a rupture in the seam between people. For however David may blush and put it down, blind to its splendor (as to the physical beauty of his own arm or leg), that well-worked routine permits about fifty per cent of all boys he approaches to have their cocks sucked by him, which is what they and he want. And out of whatever lapidary conceit I may want to show it off, also I want that line down as a text or good lesson for all Davids to come, so that they too can make openings for themselves and the boys they will blow. Save your thanks.

And if you want to know who David is, study his eyelids. The real David counterfeits sleep not to have to wake to you.

We have eaten boxes of benzedrine and have lain embraced and impotent all night long. In the morning David says softly, "What's the matter, aren't you attracted to me?" I say, "Yes, but the pills—" but he cuts me off. "You know my taste, I mean for young boys. But if there is anything you want to do. . . . I love you very much."

Is it David who says this or someone else? Someone else with the name of David.

It's only at the suture that anything interesting happens in human beings—the white silk shirt on the panhandler, castemark on his forehead (a scab). His helplessness arouses me —sadistically. I want to take him home and commit perversions on him, I want him to squeal helplessly and submit and love to submit. How I want to order these bums around. "You! Abuse yourself in front of me! That's right, pull out your dick—what a big dick you have—is it normal in bums? Now start jacking off. You already have a hard-on so it shouldn't be hard. Do you stand around all day in a slouchy overcoat, too ashamed to own the big bulge in your trousers, which are always unbuckled?"

Or that is a two-day-old or three-day-old shirt being worn by the office manager, the dirty shirt that doesn't fit the costume, the seam, that saves him, the catch or stitch that makes people bleat or bowl over.

Obsessions! Perversions! Sweet Ennui of Will! The flaming flagrant queenliness that can sometimes save a man so well it makes my forehead yearn to be queened! These black angels keep us enfolded like bat kittens in their fragrant warm wings. We would sell ourselves gladly for those three-hour luncheons with plenty of olives, but the IBM's and CIA's won't have us. They won't even look in our eyes and are already buzzing for bouncers—our mama black angels have scared them off keeping us pure.

The Poet! The Crooked! The Extra-fingered! The tendon stitched onto the bone—the strain—the ligaments of palm and wrist—the wedding-ring muscles. Clench your fist and feed us some knuckles.

In the seam, in the change or scar. If you want to know who David is handle the wrists of every David you ever met. Handle and see. The wrong David hath no scars. In the sore. In the catch or snag, wart bubble or pimple, botch or God's mark.

Part Six

54

TROCCHI'S PAD

KINKY CAME OVER one night to show off his first needle-marks. He turned the corners of his mouth down like a tough and said, "I been shootin up with Trocchi." While I was pretending to be curious and medical, palping the veins of that smooth muscular arm, the door knocked again. It was a lady friend I had not seen for weeks, and straightaway we plunged into talk of Dresden delicacies and other fili-grees. One by one I showed her the etched glass head of a woman with long hair streaming, a pair of Benjamin Frank-lin sun spectacles, a small bone carving of a man at a table engraved with geometric patterns, an ampoule of pure pea-cock oil, and a tiny magnifying glass—the lens of a shark eye in a gold mounting. Then I said, "Now do you want to see something very fine and precious?" She nodded deli-ciously. I took hold of Kinky's arm and rotated it outward, showing her the crook. Kinky gasped, and my lady friend laughed. He went home shortly afterwards, leaving me and her (so he must have thought) to talk of spider bites and tiny fingernail scratches.

The next time I saw Kinky he was courting the lunatic asylum. He had been shooting amphetamine into that beauti-ful arm six times a day for weeks, and he was so scared and shaken he wouldn't walk down the street alone, and he kept telling me to lower my voice for fear the police were listening. He looked as though he were struggling to escape through his eyes and go straight out the window crashing through glass. He knew he had to pull himself together, for he was a dancer expecting to be called any day, and afraid to go home (he lived with his parents). On his promise to give up amphetamine till he was over the jitters, I gave him the key to David's apartment (David was visiting his psychiatrist in Needles). A few days later, on my way to Salinas, I stopped by to see how Kinky was doing, but he was out, and I left him a note. When I returned to the city, I found the following note under my door:

Dear Sheeper,

Thanks for letting me use David's place. Many things have happened since you came over Monday night when I did not see you. I have my own place on Bdellatomy Avenue —135 Bdellatomy Avenue, apartment 5. But—

I got a call to go on tour with the American Ballet Theatre. We are leaving tomorrow morning so I guess I won't see you before I go. I am giving my pad to Alex Trocchi while I'm gone. The rent is $26 a month for 3 rooms. I must go now. David's key is on the ledge above the door. That's all.

Love,
Kinky

Two weeks later I found another note under the door, this one from Allen:

Sheeper—I am by to visit—no one home—a MOST remarkable scene is taking place at Alex Trocchi's pad at 135 Bdel-

latomy Avenue, 2nd floor left of stairway, "Musee Imaginaire" sign on the door—go by for five minutes—Allen

I had planned to visit Trocchi's one Monday evening. Late
the afternoon of the projected visit, I myself was paid a call
by a strange and interesting boy who had just been paroled
from the Farm. He was about seventeen, fair and beardless,
with a disarming shyness and almost feminine beauty that
would make one want to write to the Commissioner of Cor-
rection praising our penal system, if one didn't know that
this boy had been an outlaw in jail and had beat the system
by strength of will and accident of love. This was "Rimbawd," who had been Roy's cellmate for two years and had
turned into a girl for him, and whom Roy had turned into a
poet. Rimbawd was the protagonist of a brilliant story of
Roy's, and I was awed and embarrassed talking to the boy,
and curious as to what in him had ignited Roy, and afraid to
find out. Begetters of poetry are like the seraphim, who are
called burning or kindling, and shouldn't be looked at by
pale men like me without dark glasses.

Rimbawd's physical presence was frankly unnerving, and
I was relieved by another knock on the door, hoping that the
new visitor would reduce the tension that had built up
between Rimbawd and me.

This hope was based on the happy sexual life I was at that
time leading. For a long time I had been up nights in deep,
intimate conversation with a series of new boyfriends, but
nothing ever happened. Things somehow always got too nervous. After saying goodnight I used to look at myself in the
mirror and wonder whither my charm had flown. In fact I
had collected so many new boyfriends that pretty soon they
were walking in on each other. At first I was alarmed and

disheartened when, after three hours of talk which grew
more and more frantic and sexual, a friend and I were interrupted by knocks on the door. But I soon discovered that the
presence of a third person so reduced the tension and
awkwardness that had grown up beside the longings of just
two of us, that what could not have taken place with two,
came to pass often with three.

But the welcome intruder on Rimbawd and me proved to
be Smilowitz, whose appearance dashed all hopes for ease
and intimacy, for he notoriously made people uncomfortable.

He was small and dark, with a hooked nose and small,
nearly shut mummy eyelids, which his head was always tilted
back to see through. He seemed always to be drowsing. His
movements were graceful but so delayed they seemed to take
place in a slow-motion world. It is as if he were keeping his
body underwater to quench his eyes, which reacted to everything nervously and hungrily. First his eyes would light on
a new object of interest. If his interest continued, then his
head would rotate slowly to ease the strain on his eyeballs.
Finally the rest of his body would adjust appropriately or
perform some action, smoothly and lumberingly, with the
same threat of speed a mantis has. He never turned his head
merely to look at something he could see by moving his eyes
alone, and there were times when those eyes followed my
movements a little too closely for comfort, and I would fight
back by stepping right out of his eyeshot, thus forcing him to
move his head quickly in order to give his eyes back their
vantage.

He was as sparing of speech as of movement, and he
always spoke through clenched teeth, reluctantly and with an
odd explosiveness necessary to force the words out through
his shells and barriers. He never made conversation, though

occasionally he made observations, which fascinated me with their terseness or strange utter banality. He would interrupt a long thoughtful silence in a room full of people with a remark about the weather. It was difficult to know when he meant to be funny; he never smiled. He turned on my faucet one hot summer night for a cold glass of water, but the tenement water pressure had dropped almost to nothing. He said: "My faucet leaks more than your faucet gives."

In a group sometimes he would pick out a beautiful woman to stare at all evening long, often discomfiting her, and then, after she had said her round of goodnights and the door had been opened for her departure, he would suddenly face her full, his coat on his arm, and utter: "Can I walk you home?" And the next day or day after, sitting with the poor girl over some hot tea and cookies, I would make certain excuses for my friend's strange behavior, and speak of his virtues to help him a bit with his forlorn suit. And she, if she were kind, would say, "I agree he is the most non-imitative person I have ever seen . . . and reminds me less of any other human being than anyone I know," and would make quick to change the subject.

After Smilowitz had settled into a comfortable chair, with a pipeful of marijuana and a cup of smoke-tea, Rimbawd continued talking about Roy, evenly and tensely. He flooded us with jail memories of sex and tenderness, and then he said, "I know I'm a man as much as anyone, and as hungry for girls as any man alive, but the truth to tell is I'm still in love with Roy and likely always will be, and I would sooner live with him, yes and sleep with him, than a harem of young cunts in bloom. But now he is out of jail and back with his Wife, and sometimes with other chicks too I think, and he has no time for me. I love him just the same and I'm proud of it. I am proud of being in love with a man like that. Until I met Roy I had a pretty hard time at the Farm. They used to whistle at me and call me Grace Kelly. And you know how it is in jail—you always have to do what they want, or else. The first time I ever took a shower, I got, you know, fucked by four guys. They kept me a prisoner in the shower room. O.K. and I'll tell you I wiggled my hips too, and bit their necks, and stuck my finger up their assholes while they were screwing me, to give each one the best pleasure I could, because I was afraid they would kill me. I met Roy in the library one day. He put his hand on my ass. He was a big shot—gallery representative in the Prison Council. When his cellmate got paroled, he had the right to choose another one. There were a bunch of us standing around the day room, all looking at him, hoping he would choose us. He just pointed at me with his little finger. I guess you know the rest from his story. We started reading books together. He encouraged me to write poetry, and he was tough on me, hard as hell to please. I would show him a poem, and if he didn't like it, he would tear it up, or tell me it was shitty, or sometimes he wouldn't speak to me for a whole day. That was the worst punishment of all. I couldn't stand it, and would plead with him to say some little something. I figure he taught me everything of importance that I know, about poetry and everything else."

And indeed once I had asked Roy, when I foresaw the end coming between David and me, how he managed to hold his Wife to him so closely. "Not only your Wife, but you always have a fleet of girls in tow besides. How do you do it? I can't seem to hold anybody." Roy smiled at me gently and said, "Well the way to hold on to a girl is to be cool. I'm indifferent to them, see, and they know it and keep after me. I ig-

nore them and they come back for more. . . . Do you want to
know how to hold on to a girl or how to hold on to a boy?"
"A boy," I allowed. "To hold a boy," he said softly, "you
have to teach him something."

Rimbawd spoke mainly to me, yet once in a while he
would shoot a long probing glance at Smilowitz, who re-
mained absolutely silent. These glances grew still longer, and
more hostile and crafty. Finally Rimbawd interrupted himself to ask Smilowitz sharply, "Where have I seen you
before?" Smilowitz proffered not a word of reply, nor did a
muscle of his poker-face move.

RIMBAWD: I never forget a face. . . . I know I've seen this
guy somewhere before. . . . How long have you lived in the
city?
SMILOWITZ (*after a long pause*): Twenty-five years.
RIMBAWD: Have you ever been busted?
SMILOWITZ (*after a long pause*): No.
RIMBAWD: Tell the truth Smilowitz, 'fess up. Look, I've been
in jail and am not ashamed to talk about it. (*Pause.*) Did you
ever do a bit at the Farm?
SMILOWITZ (*after a long pause*): No.
RIMBAWD: Why not come clean, you'll feel better. Sheeper
won't think any the less of you. I did a bit and so have a lot
of other guys. It's nothing to be ashamed of. (*Pause.*) Was
your nickname "The Stiff"?
SMILOWITZ (*after a long pause*): No.
RIMBAWD: I know you were at the Farm, why won't you admit it? How many beds in Gallery A? (*Pause.*) Now don't
try any tricks. (*Pause.*) Answer this question: How many
beds in Gallery E? How many beds in the infirmary? Who
shoved a banana up Mother Splayfoot's keester? Let sleeping

dogs lie. We're both older and out of jail and what happened there don't mean we can't be friends. So let's be friendly. I'm just curious, that's all. Just tell me one thing. Last September, I don't remember the exact day, the whole Gallery was playing baseball. You and Roy slipped off to the cowbarn. *What did you do there?*

What vexed Smilowitz enough to alter with a frown the dead-pan I had always thought absolute? Perhaps it was the homosexual drift of the talk, or the direct imputation Rimbawd had made. Once before Smilowitz had complained of certain friends, whose remarks had led him to believe they might not greet with total incredulity the possibility that under very extenuating conditions he would not repulse with all his heart the advances of a man or young boy, be he in faultless female masquerade.

Perhaps it was the idea that he could possibly be mistaken for someone else. For it may be that Smilowitz was proud of his grotesque individuality, and how could it be other than an art or craft?

Perhaps it was divulgation of a fact he did not wish to be known, such as his tryst with Roy or the imprisonment itself. For my part, I trusted Rimbawd's accusations, for it seemed easier to suppose that Smilowitz was lying than that he could ever have been mistaken for anyone alive.

In any case, as soon as Rimbawd realized he had driven Smilowitz into a corner, his own sense of compassion and fair play prevailed. He stopped the interrogation at once and gracefully took leave of us. As he went out the door he paused and said "No hard feelings?" but Smilowitz wouldn't even look up.

I spent a long time sitting mutely with my taciturn friend, in the glare of the kitchen, and some of his gloom began drifting toward me. To dispel it, I thought I would broach a safe neutral subject and draw him into conversation.

SHEEPER: My dear Smilowitz, when I was younger, and a more serious student of the arts and several sciences, including those of the mind and its diseases, I owned every single book in the area of psychology published by Mr. Haldemann-Julius, and I used to attend every public lecture in this subject I would hear of. It was my pleasure to have attended a series of lectures by our great American psychiatrist and homespun philosopher Dr. Handy Butts. Dr. Butts always used to say, "I cure people with a little Emerson, a little Edison, and a little Eddie Cantor, haw haw haw." He practiced a form of water immersion therapy he called "nothing more than a good old Southern baptism," and he pounded the pulpit and loosened his string tie and told the audience in a low whisky whisper: "If I have seen farther than my predecessors, it was because I was standing on the shoulders of God." Well Dr. Butts used to give demonstrations of his informal American psychotherapy, sometimes playing the role of the psychiatrist—I remember he would open each session with a dirty joke—and sometimes playing the role of the patient, with one of his own students as the psychiatrist. That doctor was such a simple honest man he would talk about his own personal problems right there on stage in front of the whole audience, human things, like his wife not liking him to beat his meat in front of her. And he would use his own student, a novice in the study of the human mind, to help him solve his problems. Now Smilowitz I don't mean to imply that you're a novice or student of mine in any sense, but I want you to help me solve a problem in my own field, and I know you can do it, even though you haven't given this field much thought or attention. My field is making notes.

Sometimes, when reading my notes, I misread certain words, and I almost invariably prefer my mistakes to the words as originally written, even though the new meaning be a serious distortion of the old one. As you may know, there is a philosophy afloat that good notes are incorrigible in every sense, and any emendation is a warp or gloss over the truth dictated by the Muse or Eye that seeth all at once. But my corrections are commanded to me too, and which Muse can I trust? Yet when I turn from the problem in the abstract and try to solve it *ad hominem,* accepting for mine the viewpoint held by the man I can trust, another set of problems stops me in the face. For example, my friend Allen, whom I trust in most matters, is a fanatical exponent of unretouched note-making, and yet, and I tell you this in the strictest confidence, he models his own notes arduously. But I know better than to judge an apostle by the very doctrine he promulgates—if he believed himself he would shut up already and stop proselytizing. Smilowitz, help me, I am lost in a labyrinth of my own wisdom. Just tell me, shall I alter my notes or leave them be?

SMILOWITZ *(after a long pause)*: Only you could know.

SHEEPER: O don't be laconic at a time like this! . . . All right, finish the sentence at least to prove you've been listening: Who could know what?

SMILOWITZ *(after a long pause)*: Anything.

SHEEPER: But what do you mean?

SMILOWITZ *(after a long pause)*: You know what.

SHEEPER: Zip down your fly and be human for once. I respect your purity, but small talk is important as a web between people or Archangel agar human beings flow out to each other on. For myself, I never listen to what anyone says anymore, just to the tone of their voices, and breathing, and the way they twist their upper lips. But you have to have a canvas for those things to appear on, that's what small talk is. Even poets at times make small talk to keep human. You bug everyone with the way you put down normal human contact and yet impose your presence everywhere so that hands keep checking legs and ankles to make sure you haven't made off with a shank or a whirl-bone. It's no good to keep denying your human nature. That's why I think any- one who hits on a line of questions that gets a rise out of you is your saviour. . . . Now that Rimbawd is gone I want you to be frank with me. How many beds in Gallery A?

SMILOWITZ (after a long pause): Why don't you invent your own questions?

SHEEPER: How many beds in Gallery E? How many beds in the infirmary?

SMILOWITZ (like a tortured animal at the end of its patience): What infirmary?

SHEEPER (after a long pause): You know what.

SMILOWITZ (after a long pause): If you don't ask something interesting, I'll ask.

SHEEPER: I don't believe it.

SMILOWITZ (after a long pause): Why don't you visit Trocchi's pad like you were going to?

SHEEPER: O.K. Smilowitz. . . . Will you go with me?

SMILOWITZ (after a long pause): No.

SHEEPER: Why not?

SMILOWITZ (after a long pause): There's no reason to.

I am locked out of the prose and have been so for days. And the inside of my cock tickles from wearing too tight pants, and knives thrust toward the center of my forehead from behind my eyes, and my asshole itches either with wanting or not wanting to be screwed, and all I can think of is shoe boxes filled with baby bats who don't know how to

fly yet, and earthen nests of female earwigs hungrily waiting
for their eggs to hatch so they can be mothers, and Huncke
about to be busted now that he is bristling with needles again
like a porcupine. And though I know I will always find
cream to lap up and be gorged with cream like a fat black
cat, think of what I have to screen out to go on with the
story. And buck the bad grace not to say dereliction of duty
of that wrinkled Muse refusing me all help and then dozing
off to sleep so frowardly. "It will have to be a construction of
your brain alone," she mumbles.

Yet for all my pluck I know I am doomed, for even if I
could go on, my fingers can tell only part of the truth—I am
under oath—and, besides, decay and dejection poisoned the
air I breathed in Trocchi's pad from the first moment I was
inside, but at that time I had to see only the good, and so
my original vision was discordant and clouded. Even the
little true beauty I picked up there, to pop in my mouth and
suck on, was mixed with a slow-acting poison to make the
eyes opaque and dreamless, and so I wandered through the
world with a black notebook I never wrote in, till the Ram
broke through the clouds and then the sway of Libra in the
heavens swang my heart to beat. No wonder the mind is
filled with nicks and nibbles, and in this jumpy and spiritless
mood, I take up my pen.

And so Smilowitz and I tumbled out into the night, and a
blue needlepoint mist blew into our faces. The street was
empty of people but littered with garbage, and we passed
a broken bookcase I almost asked Smilowitz to help me lug
home, but I gave it up so as not to have gone out falsely. We
passed a cat with a piece of raw liver in its mouth furtively
searching for a place to eat it. "Blast all cats," I said, "for
the countless hypodermic needles filled with cat dander

serum." Smilowitz stepped into the blue light of a street lamp, took out his wallet, searched through it briefly, and handed me a small printed clipping, watching my face intently as I read it. "Keep it," he said.

> A traveller, coming upon the graveyard of a ruined abbey, saw a procession of cats lowering a small coffin with a crown on it into a grave. Some weeks later he related what he had seen to a friend, and the friend's cat, who had been lying quietly curled up before the fire, on hearing the story sprang up crying out "Now I am king of the cats!"

We continued walking together right up to the door of a ramshackle tenement on Bdellatomy Avenue, where Smilowitz bade me goodnight. As I pushed the door open, a foul draft or rather blast of cockroach odor assaulted me. I made my way upstairs in the dim inner light of a vase, and the first thing I saw when I reached the second floor landing was the legend "Musée Imaginaire" in black Gothic letters, on a shirt cardboard tacked to a door. I could hear no sound from behind that door, either before I knocked or after. I waited a minute and then knocked again, and my knock was answered by a great crash just behind the door, followed by a volley of squeals, as if from women running through rooms. But no one opened the door, and I knocked again.

This time I was answered with loud scrapes and bangs, as if heavy wooden objects were being stacked against the door to barricade it. The transom was glass painted over, for I could see the gleam of a naked light bulb through a tiny spot where the paint had been scratched away. Suddenly that spot went black. An eye was watching me. Then a muffled female voice said, "Who is it?" I said, "Sheeper." Silence. A murmur of consultation. A Scottish-accented voice that must have been Trocchi's said, "Who? Sheeper? Let him in!" More wooden bangs and scrapes as what seemed to be a platform of chairs and tables up to the peephole was dismantled. Finally a latch snapped, a crack of light appeared, and the door swang open smoothly, on a tableau of Trocchi seated in a chair facing the door, squeezing the rubber bulb of a medicine dropper into his arm. He looked up at me, and I saw the pleasure spread on his face like a star. "You are a gracious man," I said.

I am in a market place that suddenly springs to life as the door closes behind me. Everyone is talking at double-time, talking drugs and trading drugs. A fifteen-year-old Porto Rican pusher seems to be auctioning off packets of heroin. A painter with only two teeth left in his mouth works furiously at an easel on which, instead of a canvas, a lady's summer coat has been stretched. He is humming happily and talking to himself as he works. A young girl seated in a chair by the door is sharpening a spike on a matchbook cover (I thought she was filing a fingernail). She looks up into my eyes and asks me what my chemistry is. I am not sure of her meaning until someone nearby says, "Chemistry, chemistry, you know man, your glands." I tell her regretfully that I am queer. The man who translated her question is standing nonchalantly naked with a hard-on I simply can't take my eyes off of.

I manage to shake hands with Trocchi. We rap a bit over the din. I tell him about Allen's note, and he says he is glad I have come, and that I should make myself at home, but that I would have to excuse him for a few minutes as he was in the middle of a lecture when I knocked on the door. He simply turned about-face and walked off.

The floor was completely littered with drawings and manuscripts, and every square inch of every sheet and scrap of paper had been utilized. Manuscript margins were filled with india ink sketches, and handwriting in all colors followed the contours of figure and symbol, giving each graphic form a strange talismanic aureola. All these papers were torn and shoeprinted and formed a thick, uncomfortable carpet. Textures of color, astronomical signs, animal forms, and Greek and Hebrew letters were painted onto the walls themselves, and these designs were partially obscured by numberless abstract paintings taped and tacked to the walls everywhere. Furniture *qua* furniture simply did not exist in the room, but in the carved and painted objects of art strewn carelessly about, one could detect a drawer knob, chair leg, or alabaster lamp base. Propped against the wall were two half-finished paintings on the head and foot boards of a dismantled bed. An old-fashioned icebox had been half-crayoned over into a Persian casque. In the corner of a beautiful batik hanging was the label of a bed sheet company. The texture of broken wood was especially favored, and large wooden splinters that had once made up chairs and tables were painted fastidiously in brilliant parti-colors. Everything functional had been drafted into the service of art, taken apart and reassembled, and many things looked subjected to more than one transformation, as if the lust to create had been so overpowering as to become cannibalistic, or as if each object of art, once created, became as stupid as a lamp or bookend, and had to be destroyed and built anew. The whole room seemed to belong to another world, to whose inhabitants these uncanny furnishings were the beds and chairs of everyday life.

Bits of conversation drifted my way. "I remember the time
I couldn't stand the sight of a needle." . . . "A user for
twelve years and never been hooked." . . . "I got beat for a
fiver today, my last fiver, there must be a panic in this city,
and it was people I know man, good people." . . . "Man I
used to gross a hundred a day pushing pot in Needles—and
every ounce to friends I turned on myself." The toothless
painter yells out, "It's only a question of time before we're
all busted" and then he laughs insanely. A windowshade flies
up. Two girls rush to the window looking for cops.

Six or seven people stand round a sink in the corner
waiting to shoot up. Only one dropper is functioning. The
rest are clogged, leaning in a glass of water like a few stalks
of lily-of-the-valley, on a glass shelf above the sink. Another
glass of water is used to rinse the dropper between fixes, and
a third glass is filled with amphetamine sulfate solution,
apparently being used in wholesale quantity. Why aren't the
clogged needles being cleaned? Obviously because everyone
enjoys standing around watching each other shoot up so
much. A seventeen-year-old boy in a brilliant white cardigan
sweater grows restless. His hair is black and glossy. There is
a long white comb in his back pocket. His eyes are black and
quiet as an angel's. He looks like a student body president.
He tilts his head mischievously and asks for a taste. He
means, can he have a fix out of turn. There is a grumble of
acquiescence, and someone hands him a full dropper, saying,
"You had two fixes already, go easy." They watch him tie,
and run a pale handsome finger down the vein he will
puncture. How tenderly he handles the needle. How indig-
nantly he refuses someone's offer to shoot him up. And now
the needle goes into the skin—blood—we are breathless. He
bolts half the dropper as if he were starving, and then slowly,
slowly he boots the last half in, now mixed with blood: he

pulses it in, to extract maximum pleasure, as in fucking. How exquisitely he shudders. He is paralyzed with pleasure, and his face is a mask of rapturous pain. Here are lusts and pleasures as pure and strong as sexual ones, and the mechanical act which accompanies them is free of *intercourse* with others (the voyeurism is gratuitous). All of us have empathic orgasms watching the boy, you can practically hear us shoot off, one after the other. Someone hungry to fix tells the boy to pull the needle out already, but the boy cannot and sinks to his knees sweating. The hungry one pulls it out for him, not kindly. The boy is a kneeling Jesus whom everyone detests and admires. Even Trocchi, returned, jerks a censorious thumb at him: "He never says anything. He won't even show us his badge." This is called cop paranoia, and it wanders through the apartment like anybody else.

The hungry one who shoots up next is a bodybuilder with huge blue flower tattoos on his arms. He is straight from a health magazine cover and makes Trocchi standing beside him look even more gaunt and wasted. He has punctured his skin and is pushing the needle through a vein wall. His face is screwed up, and the pounds of meat on his arms and back are contracting clonically. All his huge mammal strength is being used to force the shyest cock in the world into the greediest asshole. Between the big twitches of his muscles there are easier trembles like flowers. Is it a miss? Slowly a red curl of blood rises in the dropper, and we start breathing again. And as he squeezes the rubber bulb, all of us feel the drug hit our brains, in as close empathy with each other's pleasure as with his. I am drowning in forbidden pleasure in an orgy I don't even know how I got into. . . .

A pair of pants drops to the floor. A Negro, nude from the waist down, is handing Trocchi a full dropper. He has grabbed a hunk of his own black buttock and tells Trocchi to fix him there. He apologizes to us spectators for descending to a skin pop, but, he explains sadly, he has no veins left at all. Trocchi looks at the dropper grumbling "It's a lot of shit for a skin pop" and jabs him with no more ado. The Negro rubs his buttock up and down, up and down, I guess to work the drug into his tissues.

A light rap on the door freezes the room. Silence. Only the painter continues working unconcerned. "It's the fuzz—" he says, "—the space fuzz—heh heh heh heh hee hee hee." He cackles toothlessly to himself never once looking up from his "canvas." Someone starts stacking chairs and suitcases, a girl clambers up to the peephole and says, "It's Tessa." As the scaffold is dismantled, a long argument takes place at the door as to whether or not Tessa should be admitted. "I saw her talking to the fuzz in a patrol car yesterday," says one. "Aw let her in," says another. Finally the door is unlocked, and while a woman reaching into the group standing at the door screams "Don't let her get by," a tiny emaciated girl in a picture hat and huge handbag, as if she were playing mama, pushes her way in, saying, "I came just to use the bathroom—do you mind if I take a pee?" One of the girls tries to pull her out, but Tessa resists, her hat pushed back precariously, and finally they let her stay. She walks over to an unoccupied spot of floor by a wall, sits down crosslegged, and has a private picnic of peanuts from her handbag, into which she drops the shells. She is now perfectly at home, with the same rights and privileges as anyone else, and in a little while she gets up and walks to where a broken table is lying upside-down. She takes off her overcoat and throws it down inside the table top to make a nest, into which she tries to settle, but one leg is in the way. She grabs a totem pole lying nearby and starts banging the offending leg with it, in order to break it off. She makes so much noise that someone stops her, but she begins banging again as soon as he walks away, and to the next person who tries to stop her she patiently explains that she is making herself a bed, as she is terribly, terribly tired. Finally Trocchi himself wrenches the pole from her, and she acquiesces, settling into the table top as comfortably as she can. Just as she closes her eyes, the Negro asks if she wants to go cop with him. She says, "I am terribly, terribly tired. Are you going where that would be apropos?" He is not. She tries to sleep but cannot, and before long sits up and asks if there is any food about. Someone asks her if she would like pancakes, she nods, and to the rallying cry "Tessa has ordered pancakes" all the chicks who were arguing at the door, both for and against her entry, are at the sink reading recipes and mixing batter. They soon tire of the project and call Tessa in to finish making her own pancakes. The batter looks grey to me, but I guess not to Tessa, who thinks it is eggs she begins scrambling, standing in the kitchen with a handkerchief tied around her head out of habit—for the hair she had once shaved off and then was ashamed of being seen without had all grown back. A man standing near me, watching that frail girl mix her batter, wonders out loud, "What would she look like pregnant?"

The toothless painter turns his attention to me, I cringe. "I'll sell you my best painting for your coat." On the one hand I plead that it is my only coat, on the other hand I ask to see his best painting. He throws a hand down, that could be in contempt of my equivocating, and disappears into the crowd. I think he has given me up for good, but I hear his voice a few moments later shout, "You're not even looking." He is holding a long narrow painting under his right arm. I like it immediately, and look slowly across it, till I come to his arm, whose veins are tracked with tiny red dots. "I'll sell you that much of it" (he means the amount my eye had covered) "for your sweater."

This crudeness of tactics made me want to say no and turn away, but I didn't. I suspected the painter was trying to teach me something, and I owed him respect for the effort, whatever the outcome. I thought that he was trying to make me see that any work of art was more valuable than any material thing, and that to make a point he was willing, like Solomon, to split asunder his painting. He was willing to destroy the work of art to prove to me, in my retrospect, that paintings and clothing are incommensurable. And perhaps he was trying to teach me to *act* on behalf of art instantaneously. I hesitated, thinking, caught in his paradoxes. He waited only a few seconds, and then broke the painting on his knee (it was on a wood panel), again and then again and again, into splinters. I was horrified—with myself—it took me months to think it all out. Finally I came to the conclusion that the painter had blundered and not taught me what he intended, but had ended by teaching me more than he knew.

The play of truth and moral beauty in that apartment was like lights, and Trocchi's Scotch burr scratched my heart, and for months I judged everything I saw and did as inadequate and cowardly compared to what went on in Trocchi's pad. I told myself that my version of the painter's remark would have been: "Only a question of time before we're all binned or hated (but heavens not busted)." I pilloried myself for not jabbing people in the ass openly, no, I wait around sneakily until they actually wiggle their behinds right down onto my prick and grind. Grind you motherfuckers, grind.

I used the honesty I gleaned at Trocchi's pad, there among

rats and amphetamine heads, as a model for my own life as an artist, and I dipped all my old values into a new cold acid, and many things dissolved, and I let them go gladly, and a few bright eaten-away fragments were my treasure, and I thought I was safe and straight with God forever. But I was wrong. I lived to see a whole new set of deceits and vanities take root from those fragments, degrading my life even before I realized it was in danger. Trocchi's pad and everything in it burned to the ground. Life is a long struggle against meanness and error.

BILL INDIA

To SNUGGLE DOWN for a comfortable sleep in an apartment that cannot be locked. And knowing Lilith slayeth those who sleep alone. To buck an ennui I fear was sent by the angels and must be upset. And I will blow away with my black windy powers the shimmering creatures who have planted themselves before me like Michael in flames throwing firebrands before me to blind me. Or break them in the black machinery I may need to construct for this last black chapter, mechanical drawings on construction paper, orthogonal projections to the eye that sees all angles at once, you ear that loves the hum of lathes. This monel machine part is oily to handle, do you know the tolerance it was made to?

So the mechanic lends me five dollars and a monkey suit all washed and ironed by his mother, sits down right beside me on the bed, and starts drawing all the tools I will need to know, printing the name of each one below it. "Tell them you worked at Bethlehem for a year and they laid you off. They won't check. It's an easy job, you won't have no trouble. The machinist tells you what tool he wants and you hand it to him. You might have to unscrew a few nuts. Oh yeah, it's cold out there, dress warm."

I may need to invoke all the power shafts and sneaky

elliptical gears I know of and sequin cams embedded in the asphalt, damp with oil.

So the gas station attendant shows me how to sew cord rings around fishing pole handles and tells me I can charge fishermen ten cents apiece, another mechanic kind to me when I was ten or eleven, we sat in a small glass office the California sun poured into, and he used to smile at the customers and wipe their windshields with a wet grey chamois, while I jealously used to hope the cars wouldn't need oil or water. How I hate to be left even for a moment.

Ah gentle reader, where were you when my arm was nearly twisted off behind me in that school in which you too were a pupil? Where were you when the last bone was broken, and I swore the testament of my criminality to beings in whose existence I was afraid to believe? I had only the toy shield of my fancies to cower under. I have fallen to my knees before every man. I have sent out summonses and salvation pleas. I have blasted my loneliness turning to grief into cities and men's minds they don't want it to enter. Need I print this in "day-glo" to make it stand out? To whom else can I scream but the centuries?

I say, I may need to invoke these black grimy arts, which keep turning harmless bafflingly, as if they knew I were going to paint Bill India not with dread and hatred, but with all the initial wonder that rained down on me like hammers the first few times I saw him.

Three men fought on the same side in a long perilous war. They were scarred and crippled but survived. They made a solemn mutual pledge to hold their silence about what they had seen, since they believed that no account of it could accrue to the good of the human race, whose welfare they genuinely wished to improve. Each man was afraid that his

account would inadvertently make evil seem attractive and
even triumphant, for they all believed that evil *had* tri-
umphed, though they were too proud to say this explicitly to
each other. And too frightened. In particular they wanted no
portrait of Bill India to appear in print, for they recognized
his stature though they hated him—they gave the devil his
due—and they were afraid of graving an image that wicked
men would see across deserts of time, and bow to. I know
it has been for reasons allied to these that I have idly capped
and uncapped my pen for so many weeks, that my Muse left
me flat, that my mind even now seethes with earwigs and
white ants. I think I am being pushed forward by Satan, who
singeth to me of the natural identity of his goals and the
good of mankind, whose voice I heed, whose persuasion I
yield to. What we were once dead-set to suppress will be
bared. Just as I know it is possible for some people to be
good and yet call up evil, with which they battle long and
courageously (gathering weak souls about them whom they
prop up), so that when they die or leave town Pharaonic
plagues of meanness and destruction triumph everywhere, so I
hope it possible for a black course unswerving, in shearing the
heavy water, to leave a white wake and spume. But no more
do-good apologies. Let that oath I once made break apart,
and I will force one of the other two veterans into a kind of
moral collusion with me, for I have all his wartime notebooks, and will quote from them in due course.

I had heard the name Bill India once or twice before, and
remembered nothing in connection with it but that he was
thought to be strange. I vaguely knew he was one of the
Street People, urban gypsies who never have pads of their
own, but move from place to place, bartering their arts and
dark glamour for a couch to sleep on, and invariably being

turned out for stealing or destroying their host's property. Either they are turned out or their host becomes a ghoul like them, soon to be evicted himself by an outraged landlord who has called the police. Trocchi discovered and befriended him, and made him Vizier of his life and pad, and that Vizier more or less invented Trocchi's pad, though I did not know it the night of my visit, Trocchi mentioning Bill India only as a friend expected later.

Trocchi gave Bill India a freer reign than he had ever had before, and nourished and abetted his excesses—Trocchi's bent had always been editing—but to his own pad he himself retained the key, and so Bill India flowered yet not fully. After Trocchi's pad went up in flames, I saw a succession of apartments in which Bill India was the nominal guest, and I saw his hold over each successive host tighten, as he came into his own, and I saw the final apartment (he rented himself) by candlelight, during a flash raid we conducted to liberate one of his captives—and that pad he ruled absolutely, like a sachem or potentate, in the most unearthly opulence mind can imagine.

The Web of Beauty. We expected a room whose walls were tacked with Bill India's stained and painted hangings, not a rocky grotto through whose hangings we could see deeper recesses where brown smoke and opal mist fumed up everywhere, and in the black smoke a flash of flames. Candlelight shone through huge silks and gossamers thrown on gleaming copper wires that were strung at all angles everywhere across the room. Leading off and down from these wires were another set, which converged on and were fastened to a brass chain tightly wound around the ankle of an ivory foot—which belonged to Bill India asleep on the floor. There was the Enemy in black pants and sweater, barefoot and face turned up snoring, one hand on his chest and one hand open, rather like an undernourished child home from saloogie, his face smudged with dirt. I touched one of the lead-off wires lightly, to test his slumber, and found it deep. Perhaps he had been drugged by one of our agents, for sleep was an indulgence he almost never permitted himself. Even in peacetime he slept rarely and fitfully, and I have never seen a man so hungry to stay awake.

I remember him best sitting cross-legged in the opal cloud of his possessions, his fingers working so busily you couldn't take your eyes off or quite figure out what he was doing—scraping, cutting, painting, tearing, gluing, especially smudging over anything printed clear and decisively, with his fingers always stained and sticky with his glues and inks and lacquers, wrapping tiny boxes in fur swatches, winding red threads around wand-like amulets, cooking up horse in a brass bottle cap over a candle, probing for a vein or wiping off a drop of blood with what looked like a penwiper, running a wire back and forth through a hypodermic needle, fingering the holes of his flute but not blowing it, or nervously flipping through the pages of the Fifth Book of Roses, his mind no doubt filled with the hexing of a black cat he hated. The floor about him was scattered with dozens of little objects of art and the tools of his trade: pens, pencils, and bamboo ink brushes, idols and amulets—many garnished with colored threads and feathers—of what seemed to be every cult and religion known to mankind, tiny boxes and bottles of drugs and dry inks, cowhorns and crystals, rat-tail files and long-nosed pliers, wrenches and sets of hypodermic needles—with which he sprayed and injected his cloths and leathers with dyes—, glass straws and a kid bag of semi-precious stones stolen right out of people's rings, dissecting probes and dental instruments, a shepherd's flute banded with copper, a dried-out kitten, three spirals of lavender incense from which great pillars of smoke rose almost unwavering, a tall gilded Buddha, a brass doorknob, an oarlock, perhaps a pound of colored candle stubs, some burning, some not, and finally a half-empty khaki knapsack, into which he could make this cloud of objects disappear in a twinkling, and from which, swung lightly with one hand from his back to the floor, he could set up shop anywhere. Each fetish had a respective ritual: a certain way of being wrapped or unwrapped in its own piece of cloth or soft kidskin, with its own string tied in certain ways and knotted in certain places: a certain order in which each was taken from the knapsack and replaced: a certain postion each one occupied in the circle of objects around him: a certain formula muttered as each Kwannon, Ganesh, or Three Wise Monkeys was set upright, prone, or propped up by a spool.

His aesthetic arrogance was total. He believed that beautiful things were more properly his than anyone else's, that his prior right to them was self-evident, and so he appropriated whatever book, spoon, or scarf he fancied, when its owner's back was turned. He quickly tired of most things and would transform them into whatever he pleased, blackening silver, cutting the gilt off book edges, painting over expensive reproductions of Goyas, Bosches, and so on. His objects vanished as rapidly as they were acquired, some he gave away outright (though never to people outside his entourage except to ensnare them), some he sold to fences or to the slummers he occasionally ran into, but most found their way into the jealous fingers of his friends and emulators, which were as light as his. A high turnover of objects took place among this group, and it was possible to come across the same broken xylophone, on successive nights, in successive hands in different parts of the city. For him the beauty of an object

comprised much more than its physical form, and he often
stole things which were dull or badly designed if he sensed
that they were prized by their owners. He never questioned
his prior right to whatever anyone held precious. Like
Professor X, he was hypergullible to what anyone let on
they adored, and it was possible to get rid of an ugly knick-
knack by handling it idly in Bill India's presence. You could
be sure he would never steal or accept what you offered him
outright.

I used to have a kitten pillow I took everywhere I went.
I took it to Vermont, where I spent some time trying to cure
the Poet with sex and housekeeping. He made the bed every
morning and plumped up the pillows, and every night before
climbing under the furs I placed my kitten pillow high on
the others to sleep on. I took that pillow wherever I went,
from the bed to an armchair I sat in, and out when I went
for a walk. One night before bedtime I quarrelled with the
Poet and stalked outside to cool off, forgetting my pillow.
When I returned he was asleep—on his side of the bed—
but with his torso aslant so his head could rest on the pillow
—pressing down extra-hard on it, even though he was sleeping. Was it love or soaking up my magic power? I told this
story to a friend. It brought tears to his eyes, even though,
he later told me, he was hurt I did not ask him what he
thought the Poet's act had meant. That pillow looked cuddly,
but was hard and harsh to the touch—harsher than the touch
of coral. When I was with others I nuzzled and stroked
it, loving and childlike, but when I was alone I kicked it
into the closet. So many people these days try to hurt us by
stealing or attacking whatever they think we hold precious,
it pays to drag around a red herring.

Bill India was guilty of the most appalling malpractice and
breach of professional ethics in the annals of fat black medi-

cal history. In plain English, he put his vast beauty-garnering
apparatus entirely in the service of evil. His heart's desire
was to spread misery and suffering wherever he could, to
plunder anything precious, and to smother any flame he saw
kindling in souls. His hatred for anything human was the
fount of his art and life. His art was compulsive and so in
that sense true and even superb, but the compulsion came
from a realization fit to be made by the Black One himself—
that the road to reach souls Heavenward flaming is beauty
alone. Bill India's sights were monstrously high. And all
through that long war my cohorts and I knew we were
wrestling not with flesh and blood, but with Principalities
and Powers. Any one of Bill India's objects had the look of a
trout-fly about it.

The roots of beauty are sunk in meanness and despair as
everyone knows, and the more stinkingly black the mulch,
the more orange and burning the sunflower. Evil lengthens
the runway for the jet plane of beauty to race on before it
can rise. O give beauty the gun! Thus evil is yoked in the
service of art, and the poet a powerful magician indeed, that
he sits on Satan's neck. And everyone knows that beauty is
a living and breathing. It makes us gasp. It fills us with
light. It lasts for many lifetimes. It keeps what is tender from
dying. It is stronger than steel and towers. It is moonlight
on a lonely field, and a strong familiar pressure. You pull
open your pants in the moonlight and sink to your knees.
O touch the coolth and sleeping peaceful world in the only
way ye know how! Evil is the root and not the fleshy flower.

The Web of Drugs. Bill India was a pusher, mainly of
amphetamine, but also of pot and heroin when he had a little
more money and the chance to buy these without looking
for them. Now most heroin pushers are addicts themselves

who have gone into business to afford their habits—some love junk so much they want to turn on the whole world out of pure benevolence, I met a diversified-line pusher who was that or close to it, and I drank up his philosophy—but amphetamine was so cheap at that time relative to horse, nobody would push it just to afford it. Bill India pushed it to have something people wanted, and you can imagine he extracted all the petty suffering he could from his customers, without actually losing them, before he would come across with the drug.

The Street People came to be dubbed the Amphetamine People, and there is no question that their arts and habits were in a large part the effects of this drug. Amphetamine is thought to be a chemodepressor of the evil-inhibitory centers in the medulla oblongata.

The Web of Magic. One day Bill India happened to mention that he knew a way to make make pot four times as strong. I asked him how he did it, and he said he would come by the next morning to show me. He arrived very early, and plucked a piece of folded copper foil from between his foot and shoe. He opened up the foil, took the envelope of pot I held out to him, and poured it all out on the foil which he then folded up. He dropped the bright little packet into my palm and said, "Keep it in your mouth for four days and the pot will be four times stronger."

Yes, Bill India could come on as charming and boyish as you please, his eyes filled with innocent mischief, "Aw shucks my uncle Teddy gave me a wizard set for Christmas and I done practiced up a few tricks to show you, say you know where I can buy a baby rabbit?" But he practiced black magic and prayed to the Devil.

At first you scoffed at the magic he purported to know, for when he blew up at one of his confederates he would rush to a book, throw it open and flip through its pages muttering, as if he were searching for the formula of an especially drastic curse, but though you heard plenty of threats and unbelievably foul language, you would never actually witness the laying of a curse. Then too he used to carry tomes of ancient lore around with him like Kathy Pleune used to carry the classics of literature, not to read but as a badge of identity. It was almost comical to watch him show off that succession of books—a history of witchcraft or journal of psychic research, the *Zohar, Book of Changes, Diamond Sutra,* or Tibetan *Book of the Dead, Isis Revealed* or the *American Ephemeris* —and pretend he was steeping himself in magical wisdom, when I knew he just looked at the pictures. But, just as Kathy Pleune had the finest native literary sensibility I ever came across in a female, and she was only sixteen, at least the possibility existed that alongside all of Bill India's patent posing and hocus-pocus—and even using it to hide behind— a soul did exist which could throw a mean curse if it wanted.

And so in spite of your telling yourself Bill India was just a good showman, in spite of your natural skepticism, in spite of your devotion to the natural sciences, in spite of your life-long struggle and victory over your suggestibility, in spite of Bill India's open admission that his magic worked only on people who believed in it to begin with, you could feel yourself falling. And besides deluging you with hints of his vast arcane resources and the visual reality of his symbols and rituals, he was quick to exploit anything that happened to you in your daily life, good or bad—the arrival of your income tax refund or the death of a friend—, by implying he had brought it about for a specific plausible reason, which he was reluctant to divulge. Slowly and subtly he suggested that your life was under his influence. And no sooner did you half-believe in his magic than it started tormenting you.

You could always tell if Bill India had ever been in a room you entered, because if he had, there was sure to be an aleph or a lamed painted in blue or black or silver, on the back of a door or inside a phonograph, or the sign of Aries or Libra on the wall above a mirror, or you are suddenly facing the ideogram *chien* (obstruction) when you sit down on the toilet. Trocchi's pad and the ones that followed it were filled with these devices, as if a recalcitrant young djinn at the table had hurled, through the several apartments, a ladle of Occult Alphabet soup. A tiny aleph on your bedroom wall becomes an India henchman. It will not let you ignore it nor think of it as a pretty design, as at first. It writhes. It invites you to suffer with it opulently.

He saw himself as a kind of fallen angel, in light moods as a naughty Loki, and in black moods as the Prince of Light himself. Either way he felt himself committed to mischief and malevolence, and he did all he could to increase the horror and confusion of the people around him. His aims or rather targets were lofty, and his dedication truly epic. Let the centuries know a great black prince passed here.

56

HUNCKE'S BILL INDIA

THE PERSON TO BLAME for introducing me to Bill India in the first place was Huncke, who staggered into my apartment one day with a hanging of Bill India's over his arm. He stood there like an Arab merchant while I let my eyes be drawn through green and blue eons of time and primeval steam to where a Magic Circle glints and wheels through the air. A green light from the cloth bathes Huncke's face. His pupils are dilated. He is more lost in the cloth than I am. He whispers, "Man, it's hypodermic!" With a tremor of gratitude, a golden aleph leaps from that Circle onto his forehead.

Huncke was one of the three men who signed the pact of silence I have broken. Let him speak now with me, which he can hardly object to, since his notebooks are in my possession. Imagine that he has just fixed himself, that he is prone on a low divan, his legs crossed, his head propped up on one elbow, that he is writing, and that he stops every now and then to take a long, easy drag on a marijuana cigarette. He is a small man with a carefully trimmed beard. You should be very still, because if he hears you and looks up from writing, you stand a chance of getting lost in those amethyst eyes:

Alone—one candle burning in a tall tapering wrought

iron holder—a white paraffin candle—Wagner on the phonograph—an overture and Venusberg Music—Tannhauser—writing—with red ink—my favorite color ink—occasionally pausing—glancing from one strange, intriguing scene to another—squares of stained materials—cottons—linens—heavy paper—thin paper—oiled after hand movements—flute blowing—pot—a shot—Charlie Parker—'Hot House'—color applied with light swinging gestures—rubbing a thumb through the wet green or blue—red—violet—ink—mercurochrome—gentian violet—iodine—patterns becoming visible—universal Gods—Temples—wayside resting places—caverns and caves—animals from another planet—steaming jungles—monkies—baboons—huge monolithic beasts—intense glowing green—brilliant persian blue—writhing black—shadows—the face of a lion—tiger—part of the head of an elephant—an eye—eyes. I have seen all this and much more—in one large, square hanging—now folded —or perhaps—upon consideration—is spread out near Trocchi—great—also there are bottles bound and wrapped —bright Turkish red silk threads—black—blue—white—squares of soft kid—goatskin—hides and leather thongs—pieces of brass—fountain pens—paint brushes—bits of metal—trinkets—buttons—a large piece of fur—small pelts —many of short fur—mink brown—it is frequently used to fold round books—held secure with quarter inch wide thongs of rawhide. The reverse side tanned with dyes—symbols worked in black ink—splashes of silver—long thin wavering streaks—winding—across the surface—a smokelike quality—on another fur piece—circular—a star-like geometric pattern—the skins cut into triangles—stained thoroughly with blues and mahogany red—into tones of deep red brown—symbols of silver paint—each triangle edged in silver.

All this in front of me—created and made by Bill—whose

whole existence—at this point—is a great outpouring of
energy—his whole chemical being—activated—tingling—
tensed—alert—while each moment his consciousness
searches the scene—scanning the area—picking up something—a clay idol—a knife—pencils—pens—paper—beads
—stones—gems—wire—thread—glue—bleach—material—
cloth—wood—bone—shell—everything suggesting a new
object—a new reality—a thing springing from his fingers—
hands—arms—whole body—the ever constant linking together—methedrine—pot—heroin—tranquilizers occasionally—an ever present auditory responsiveness—intonations
—talking—voice sounds—set the nerves to vibrating—he
looks for danger—usually has been scheming—he is immediately defensive. He becomes irritated easily—is fretful
—dogmatic—somehow unaware of how to accept the moment in peace—rather—he grabs each instant—making a
challenge of everything—relaxing seldom—never for long
—then in restlessness—disturbed slumber—mutterings—
once in a while in a chair—lolled back—eyes closed—now
and then fluttering lids—deep breathing—interrupted with
an hissing sigh—cry-like sounds—a sort of moan—rolling
the head with the rest of the torso slowly in swaying motion.

Picking up the flute he stands up—carefully adjusts the
mouth to his—blows once—twice—followed by a series of
sharp quick flute notes—takes a few steps—meanwhile rip-
pling his fingers over the air holes. Again stops and begins
blowing—along with the record of Charlie Parker—Bud
Powell—preferably—with any music—or without music—
wandering back and forth—never looking directly toward
one—yet seeing every detail—of one's surface conduct—
catching hints of what has happened inside one's self. He
doesn't spend much time investigating the causes—accepting
his own responses as correct—not necessarily completely
aware—yet sure of the meaning—without all the details—

glossing over the omittance—rather superiorly—sure he has at some point passed through the same experience—nothing can be new—even allowing for personality differences—.

His magic absorbs his spirit—black magic—white magic —Gods and Demons. He practices magic—creating. He reads about the formulas—he knows the forces to command —he calls upon the planets—the moon—the animals—the spirits of wood—metal—stone—earth—of all things— watching for signs—letter combinations—numerical values —good omens—bad omens. Hearing him blow the day into radiance—the sunlight out of the morning sky—walking the lower east side streets—the flute sweet—clear and haunting. The shepherd greeting the first faint rays of light washing away the dark—giving thanks—to the world—mountains— rivers—streams—the flowers—the trees—the rocks—to all nature—.

This extract from a notebook of Huncke's is dated less than a week before the outbreak of hostilities. There is another, later sketch of Bill India, not so idyllic, to which is appended an elaborately drawn hex sign. Huncke had decided to fight fire with fire and was actually boning up on magic at the library, but his studies were interrupted by an arrest for grand larceny and possession of burglary tools.

Bill India so subverted beauty that for months after the war we found anything beautiful suspect. We were plunged into a frantic aesthetic paranoia, and avoided all baubles and art galleries scrupulously. And the secret pleasure with which each of us had contemplated the subject of magic vanished. That mysterious reservoir from which we Jews are allowed an occasional sip, and from which we artists draw the water to moisten our colors, dried up. Bill India burned the magic out of magic. Even the word sounds flat and dry

57

THE DEATH OF ELISE

I S BILL INDIA TO BLAME for the death of Elise? Whatever passed between them before I came on the scene will probably never be told, but our side was her cause, and she never flagged or complained. After the war she just walked away. She walked out of the hospital and fell on the grass, dead, of wounds incurred in a battle she fought nearly unaided while in a nearby closet I and my generals plotted. Her spirit, drifting upward in the empty space, condensed into the five tiny stars that form the constellation Brilliant Sister. I kept all her worldly belongings for a year, then gave away her clothes and books and burned her papers. I saved a small empty notebook to remember her by. The notebook has a pretty, grey lizard cover, and is perfectly blank except for three lines written in pencil on a page near the back. The lines read as follows:

> *My brother! My brother!*
> *Where is my shining brother?*
> *Lost behind the stairs.*

Her most precious objects were a wool Afghan she had made as a child, a mahogany record player her parents had given her, and a carved oak cabinet lined with white glass.

253

How she slept at night not being able to sleep deeply at all, without undressing, as if she were taking a nap, with her wool Afghan over her that I now wear on my shoulders in bed on a cold March morning with another star or beauty asleep in the next room whom I woke myself up to throw an extra blanket on, in honor of her who would always think to do such a thing. But how can I write or shine when she has killed herself, and I was not kind or loving enough to her when she was alive because I was held off by her aloofness.

Leo said she fell from her window reaching for an invisible microphone. (She thought her room was bugged and her brain was being tapped.) Huncke wrote sadly from jail that she may have been reaching for something, but not as prosaic as a microphone. (Like when Ed Marshall said it was an Apache male model and David wrote that Ed would tell me wrong, he was a Navajo.)

I called her father to ask how she was, and she answered the telephone, home from the hospital against the advice of psychiatrists. She told me that her thoughts were being tapped, the telephone too, and that she was not ready to see anyone yet. I asked her to send me a postcard when she felt like having lunch with me or going to the museum. I didn't tell her that Huncke was back in jail, and lied that he was working and happy.

She sent me a letter with a thirty-dollar money order a week before she died, telling me that was part of what she owed me—her income tax return had come. And she thanked me for my kindnesses to her (they were so few and had cost me so little) and told me to burn brightly and fiercely like a sun, for my glow to burst the troll Americanus.

58

SPIDERISM

A SPIDER is a fat black doctor who wants to hurt or de-stroy you. He is not satisfied to hit you over the head with a club of stars, he wants to roll you while you are out. He makes bait of the beauty he traps or manufactures. And when you are caught helplessly in his aesthetic web he runs over light as a touch of come to suck out your juices. The beauty a Spider traps or manufactures for his predatory ends is indistinguishable from beauty used as an end in itself or as something to give people pleasure because you like them. In other words Spider beauty is every bit as beautiful as innocu-ous beauty—and often more interesting because of the challenge to beat the Spider at his game, to con him out of his goodies without being victimized or suffering even a scratch. Not only that, but Spiderism itself can be the neces-sary taint of evil or ugliness which, by dropping the floor, uplifts our souls into arches, and turns the baubles a Spider collects into stars.

A young lady Spider down on her luck or just plain in-competent may marry to have a child of her own she can prey on. Especially one who has just arrived in a big U.S. city from Warsaw or a small town in Iowa and got a job as a seamstress and is wasting away with loneliness and beauty glut. She tells her young son, "I want to give you all the

beautiful things in life I never had, plenty of food—here, eat
another lamb chop—, piano lessons—you only practiced a
half hour yesterday and you know what we paid for that
piano—, an allowance all your own—I'll be goddammed if
you spend any of my hard-earned money on those whores
and sluts you meet in school, you have plenty of time to go
out with girls yet."

All Spiders I have known and become entangled with
have been non-verbal, or their area of Spideriness has not
involved word beauty *per se.* I have encountered several vari-
eties of eye Spiders and sex Spiders, and one ear Spider. They
almost always hate words and panic at the thought of being
spellbound, and there is no sweeter Spider prey than a
writer, whom they lure away from his work into ever more
glittering visual fields and every time he wants to sit down
and write a little they show him rainbow spectacles even
more dazzling till he has been zombified into a full-time
spectator. One of the most brilliant writers alive when I am
alive was ruined by running into a Spider who convinced
him that precious new meanings would pour forth if the
writer chopped up each day's work with a scissor and re-
arranged the confetti at random. It is tempting to conclude
that the word is with God, but I would warn the reader
against dropping his guard. I have two or three poets for
lunch with a barrel of beer, and I may stomp through my
castle breaking all kinds of webs without even knowing it,
and only one man alive can bind me with words and he is
no Spider. And I can see through prose like glass and detect
unborn spindly intentions like heat waves. The reader should
take word Spiders for granted and be vigilant, until someone
proves they cannot exist.

Why did God give me eyes to see Spiders? One night a
very large black moth He sent entered me. Black moth or
bat. Betita is an ugly black bat flying around in my brains,

you can tell by her name. Black bat or big comic book spider holding out Howie to entice me. Fatty Arbuckle is a butcher or big comic truckdriver. Marian is a little sweet brown spider running on my arm, and true to spider nature she bit me, but she really didn't mean to and it didn't hurt too much, I only hope it don't fester.

One day I am walking through the forest and a spider droppeth down before me on a web thread. I pass my magic finger before me and the spider follows it a foot below. I have him hooked. When I wiggle the finger wiggleth the spider. He tries to crawl up his thread. I bounce him down like a yo-yo, thinking to wind the silk on my fingers and watch him descend for miles. But spiders are hip to this game, they suddenly cut their thread with a scissors and drop to the ground spoiling your fun.

One day I am crossing a bridge in Vermont and from the rail I see a spider floating out in the wind on a web thread. I pass my magic finger before the rail, hook the spider and bounce him out into the wind. If this spider fucks up my fun by snipping his thread he will not fall gracefully onto a ground full of leaves he can crawl under and spin webs at his leisure, he will fall into a cold running stream and be carried away. But he is heedless and cuts his thread. A white speck falling. I lean over the rail and watch the current pull leaves under the bridge. The wind ripples the reflection of trees. The white speck touches water and skates to shore with three incredibly long light strokes.

So after the raid, with the axle-grease still on my face, that sadly half-zombified princess and I sit around rapping. She is all Canada balsam and gentian violet. From the recesses of her purple velvet kimono she pulls out a small jar of lemon blossom honey and a golden coffee spoon, and from time to time she spoons up a little honey and glomps it down gracefully. She looks up and asks if it's all right to fart. I nod politely, my index fingers hurrying into my ears. My eyes close. I start humming "Ticket Agent Ease Your Window Down" to drown out the sound. After a moment I can hear her voice, and cautiously unplug my ears. "It's all over," she says daintily, "I better light a stick of incense."

The best protection against Spiderism is prompt diagnosis. It behooves every lover of the arts, when his eye first catches the brilliant diamond facets of a new mind shining, to check out that mind for webs and sores, as David now makes a spot inspection of the cocks he blows since coming down with the clap, crabs, and two other bacterial infections at the same time. One should try to make the diagnosis vicariously —the prime rule always being to stay as far away as possible. One sign of Spiderism is the failure of an artist to release completely his own paintings or, say, photographs. Dozens of strings are hanging from them, or suddenly appear whenever someone grows interested. He will not give or sell you paintings that you like, only lend them to you. And if he lends them to you, he will begin borrowing them back or replacing them with others, always drawing you closer to him personally, and meantime hurting you as much as the aesthetic traffic will bear.

The most poignant and terrible objects of art a Spider uses for bait are beautiful souls, human beings with great graces of body or nature, whom he has preyed on and sucked out dry. They are like great empty clouds bumping lightly around him, beautiful (for the moment) to see, but with no inner being left to pad up their beauty, which sags like an atrophied face. He reaches through them like clouds. He blows them and they scatter. Their eyes are frozen. Their terror shows through the anesthesia. They are his zombies and do what he bids. He holds them out to lure new victims with. They know he counts on their beauty, and as their real beauty fades to abjectness, they

begin mimicking their former selves. What was spontaneous becomes professional. A girl who once had a love
affair with roses and carried them with her wherever
she went now picks up a rose like a robot each time she
leaves the apartment—it is part of her zombie costume. Ah,
and still you may be smitten with her loveliness, and speak to
her right there on the street, and give her your address, never
believing she will actually visit you. One day there will be a
knock on the door, and it will be she, and even though you
have meanwhile learned who she is and what you have to
fear, she makes your heart melt standing there in your hall
with her long hair wet from the rain. Maybe you think you
can rescue her from what and whom she worships. But, good
reader, if you let her in, not ten minutes will pass before you
hear another caller knocking softly and calling her name.

A zombie's old friends are even more vulnerable than his
new ones. A Spider encourages his zombies to renew all their
old friendships. Closing a zombified friend out of your life
may be like amputating a cock or finger, but it is a measure
you may have to consider.

A wise black widow will poison her victims where each
one is weakest, that is, in the pride of his strongest virtue.
But an arriviste Spider will try to reduce all his victims to his
own special sins or brand of criminality—an error which has
given more souls than one time to escape. Occasionally an
arriviste wants to show off and commit the final depravity,
which is to reform. We know one who adopted a whole pro-
gram of white thoughts—but his white thoughts were the
old tarry turds of jaundice frosted with sugar—and all
Spiders are stuck with their poor creepy selves I'm afraid.

When you have spotted a Spider, make a careful serious
appraisal of the works and objects of art which surround
him. How important are they to you? Can you get along
without them? If so, you will add years to your life by giving

the Spider, his zombies and wares, a flat absolute rejection. Throw everything you own of his out. Leave no channel open through which he can reach you. (The reader should close this book for a moment and try to determine, in the light of what has been said, and of the memoir as a whole, whether the author is a word Spider. Do this before you go on. It may be too late even now. Those readers alive when I am here no longer may want to do the exercise for fun, but there is no present danger.)

If you absolutely cannot make it, cannot live, cannot eat, cannot sleep, without possessing certain beauties of a known Spider, and you are unwilling to be zombified to get them, then brother you are at war. Even if you use an agent to get what you want, and keep your acquisitions secret, sooner or later some female you still keep in touch with, some harmless old gargoyle you used to disguise yourself with back in closet queen days, will squint her zombified eyes—what a shock—and say, "Is that one of Jerry Spider's hand-painted condoms I see sticking out from your fountain pen top?— why I didn't know you collected his work—a great artist and father confessor to me (ahem, forgive these wrinkled old tits I am always stuffing in keep falling out every time I bend over to yell right into a person's ear)—who is in fact waiting for me on the steps of the landing below—and pay no mind to these chains I have wound around you and padlocked to the bedpost as a mere mnemonic device to keep you from locking the door while I am downstairs asking him up." The best strategy is to get what you want like lightning and then split town. You could try feigning the most casual interest in the object you cannot live without, in the hopes the Spider will lay it on you to suck you in deeper. Or if you are given to bold designs, come on strong and invite him to live with you. People in general and Spiders in particular have enough

secret illegal activities in process to put them in jail. After
the Spider has moved into your pad have him busted. Or
come on as an art critic or gallery owner collecting things for
an exhibition abroad—every Spider dreams of spreading destruction as far away as Persia or the moon. O pin him right
down to the floor and make him say:

Uncle!
That I represent evil!
That the glyphs of evil all over my body leak blood!
That umbrellas open under my arms!

There are several things you can do to make our democ-
racy safe from Spiders:

1. At the first sign of a Spider warn all your friends and
fellow art-lovers. Sometimes if one or two members of your
community have been zombified, an immediate intervention
backed by the whole community can force the Spider to give
up his victims.

2. Help form a Better Beauty Bureau in your home town.

3. Never praise a Spider's work in public.

4. Keep your parlor filled with red herrings.

Finally: If you ever get into serious trouble with a Spider
you can't seem to trounce, and the traps and entanglements
spring up geometric, flee for your life. Though a Spider can
run a short stretch in a splash, he is so encumbered with
fold-away webs and boxes of costumes, gewgaws and gold
fillings, herds of sticks, clacks, and zombies, flat joints and
phony disarming dewlaps, sacks of toys, traps, and salt-water
taffy, he will not pursue you far at all. Flee, and don't stand
on false pride. You can always resume the fight later when
you are wiser and rested. Once I fled to Havana.

59

WARLOCK'S FLIGHT TO HAVANA

The first voluptuous fantasies
Of Bill India tapping a needle
Into his arm
Tapping a rubber bulb
Whack, whack—
A field of blue light
Tulips of blood.

He carried an oarlock in a paper towel
To murder with.

Oil and grime in the whorls of his fingers
We battled so close for weeks
I brought the war
To his lair, in my quarters
I and my generals plotted.

His thin body pressing my door he said
"You walk in my lair without even knocking,
Now let me in yours,
I'm a human being too."
We do not open the door

For slugs
The brass knob jiggled.

We stole her away
By candleflame

She is a princess with flaming wood hair
She twines it, shakes it out
Twists around quick
In flashes
She looks up like roses, full and pale
On her eyelids
We breathe in magenta

The silver oarlock and wooden flute
Wrapped in a paper towel
Lure me to the places
He takes off his shirt
Gold smudges his breast
Under his navel
The ivory skin.

He is my sweet
His cheeks are pale silver
He kissed me on the cheek
Behind leaves.

I wanted to pull away the spiderwebs
I wanted to see through the smoke
Of his blue socks and incense.
The drugs.

To break his spells.

This is the last time
That I will intervene
This is the last time
That I will lift from slumber
A soul
Or use a magic number

60

NATIONS

FIRST MORNING IN HAVANA the bellboy woke me up with a tiny cup of Cuban coffee and started making love to me. What could I do? He licked my asshole.

Are assholes licked licitly in Socialist countries? We hope so. We have heard the Red Army is screaming. And indeed how flourisheth homosexuality in Cuba, Russia, and Cathay? Here in Athens we wonder what will happen to culture if Philip conquers Greece. (Recently fairies holding hands on the Malecón have brought down the wrath of the barbudos. A purge of queens has taken place, though I saw no star-spangled fags on my visit there flutter. We hope the Cuban Revolution has not lost its pachanga. Havana without queens is like a copper Tropic sky without red stars.)

The caretaker of a large Cuban synagogue told me that half the congregation had fled to Miami—"the better half." When I asked what "better" meant he said "those who supported the temple." "Let them go!" I shrieked. Let them be merchants, monsters, and insurance salesmen all they want as their extracurricular occupations, collective guilt will force out a Marx or young Schleifer in time. The real job of born Jews is to stay faithful to that: to never assimilate: to teach the human race what chosen means and never trade their stock in for anything short of a full human merger.

We give up our nation when God's kingdom is established on earth. Thus I validate my Jewish birthright even though I don't know a word of Hebrew I can say where are you going? and come-on a my house in Arabic a language with a future. Scratch a gum-cracking crewcut Arab teen-ager at any American School in the Near East, and he drops his Levis before you can say ah—that good old American brainwash never quite takes. (It's a well known fact that one year at the American School doubles the earning power of young Arab boys—who apply for scholarships in droves—so many queer tourists speak English.) The state of Israel stabbed itself in the heart by kicking out the Arabs and thus robbing itself of any group estranged enough to be a spiritual reservoir for the rest—not even to speak of how in expelling them the twisted turning state abandoned its fucking sacred duty laid down on us by God. See the Tel Aviv Jews turn into goyim, like Berliner Jews did before them. It was German Jews who founded modern Israel so small in compassion—a smack in Mama Jahweh's face—hit your own mama will you—ker-blam! Meantime the new Arab nations build bigger and better atom bombs and sputniks only to throw them away thereby giving the world a dramatic example of how to live as the Koran directs.

61

SECOND COMING

NOTICE is hereby given that all claims issued by the old firm of Paul Moses and Law are now cancelled. Any requirement, therefore, to observe as a means of righteousness legal enactments bearing a date prior to your first cock crossing is a fraud and imposition.

HEAR O ISRAEL! I am too frail to tear off the veils! So I stoop to the lesser occupation. Not being able to fuck around like a man and show the love plain I am forced to show it as I can, in this crippled and style-wise fashion. Prophets are not afraid of people and spend their time plotting and preaching. To spread their word even farther they have no trouble commandeering scribes by the dozen. (In the scribe class may we place Bibiji? She is English.)

Divinity is the authority or illumination by which a prophet speaks. But his words grow old and give up the Ghost as times move on beyond the wisest foreseeable guidance. No Master foresaw that a hospital would draw water from the spring where the god Chandresvari came every night to gargle. But the parting shot of every prophet as his voice recedes beyond avail to us is "I will return" or "There will be a second coming of prophets with new God-given words to live by." Quibbling over the "real existence" of God is a pastime of the young, but the existence of such disputes is an unerring indicator that a new prophet approacheth. When the God-given rules of a community no longer strike people as intuitively true without whole Talmuds and codices attached, when every cult has a following, when each man in his heart knows the rules are wrong and a cock in his ass has rallied his soul, who can doubt a second coming is due?

The Master cancels or amends the old contracts to make it possible for the now overwhelming horde of outcasts and pariahs to live in sanity and righteousness. Their suffering calls him forth, and for them he wears the perfume of sedition, which will cost him his head while his message soareth even higher in the empty space.

Here is a dying queen riff fresh off the pen. The dying queen had sent out fifty summonses and salvation pleas to no avail. Not a single white angel showed up. So she pulled the biggest bitch fit of her career, screeching "This fucking universe needs a new Master I see," and then, out of all her anger and frustration, and using a little wire and tissue paper, she made herself a pair of huge bright wings, and she took to the public parks at night, where she would suddenly appear from behind a bush when two queers were on the ground gobbling each other, and say, "Greetings from your Sponsor! He is not pleased with the choking amateur style of your boyish disporting and hath sent me to deliver a commandment to each of ye, for He made man perfectible. Thou the big one, thy mouth could fit a horse cock to the hilt, so thou art commanded to bring thy gag reflex under control by practicing with test tubes or a young boy's cock, and art solemnly reminded that a few hours of practice will bear a lifetime of slurping pleasure. Thou the little one, thy eyes are bigger than thy rosy mouth, so be content with sucking only cock crowns, and specialize in tongue, teeth, and lip work, at the same time jerking off the cock stem with thy spit-greased fist as hard as possible. Now go to it boys, amen!"

Here is a parable for the high-minded. Jesus went out to take a piss and saw a curly-haired boy diddling himself. Jesus reached right out and grabbed that boy's cock and led him, by the cock, back to his den of disciples. The boy thought Jesus would fuck him and give him a little money but all Jesus wanted to do was kiss and feel him up. Well that was all right with the boy, so he spent the night, and by morning Jesus had him so hypnotized he left his mother and moved in with the disciples always goosing each other. But so much open love scared the boy shitless, and he asked for a little smash to split with. Just a buck would have bolstered the boy's ego enough to make him feel he hadn't been sucked dry by vampires but had been working a legitimate gig, but Jesus always trying to drench all mankind in the honey of his benevolence not a psychotic waif could escape, refused, thinking it about time the boy owned up to the love he was getting. So the boy reported him to the cops as an anarchist gang banger.

Apostles are drawn from the scum and rabble and revert to type occasionally, mistaking the Master who loves them for the Pharisees who beat them down. Or they seek Him out to hang all their woe and hopeless bungling on because nobody else would put up with them for an instant. Jesus said, "Bah, nothing rams right when Bunglebaum's around," but forgave yet again, and built his church upon his most wayward apostle, and such a blind evincing of the Master's faith made Peter rock. Judas wavered only once, and it is a sad accident of history that his betrayal made it circumstantially impossible for Jesus to make good on him as he did on Peter. Jesus come again decries the obloquy of centuries piled like shit on Judas's head. "My mistake and mine alone" the great man sighs. A prophet barely manages to hold disciples by their circumcised cock tips though he grabs for as much as he can, and it is amazing he can hang on at all, for his holy giving power is always being chewed up by demons, and he can hardly keep a step ahead of his own shit.

St. Paul of Tarsus would have been a different man had he known Jesus, and the world would have been spared another angry ruthless politician. He operated entirely by deceit and misrepresentation and polluted the Christianity he spread. He believed the end justified the means, and had himself made an Apostle though he never laid eyes on Jesus. He adopted as many masquerades as there were sects and nationalities in the ancient world, and he hungered more than any Caesar for the whole Roman Empire. We think the West would be worshipping Isis today if it weren't for him. He began his career by butchering Christians, and flipped to the other side because he saw he had more growth potential in the younger firm.

There is more sublimity in the life of Nero than in all the Pauline epistles. Being insane, Nero related himself only to the personal gratifications of the emperorship. He was fully persuaded that no such thing as a pure or honest man existed, and he ruined the whole stuffed-shirt structure of the Roman executive by treating it openly like the nest of snakes and sycophants it had been for years. Groucho Marx could not have outdone him. Not content with ruling the world, he wanted to be its foremost actor and musician, and he always had the audience packed shamelessly and himself awarded all the prizes. While he was singing, no one could leave the theater, and men would pretend to die in order to be carried out as corpses. When, with the entire Empire in revolt, he was finally forced to commit suicide, he said, "Qualis artifex pereo," what a great artist now dieth. And he was right!

The evil of Nero did not survive him. His black deeds shine pale as sea shrimp in that odd moral lesson the record of his life is. He was frank and pure and bent over backwards not to sin against the Holy Ghost. They suffer in Nashville for Paul's depravity, not Nero's.

And here is a brain trill for Alan Ansen. Highly suspicious queen rentiers clutching their pocket-books at the sound of anything good in the world, while dropping comments about how divine St. Paul's speeches are, or how much an early Greek ikon set them back, try to discredit good deeds and other living saintly acts by imputing them to selfish human motives, a logical fallacy known as Socrates' Hard-on. O burst that fallacy into Jewish stars! For human motives are not base ipso facto—no—and all saints and other highly painted men were flesh when they walked and run by lust— for thrones, for cunt, for gowns, for love and glory. These old earthy drives spawn all our good deeds like flowers. I had a dream in which I saw Alan Ansen putting on make-up at the mirror, but when I came closer I saw that he was drawing lines on his face with an eyebrow pencil. He rolled his eyes up at me shyly and said, "I will not run out and suck the first arousable cock I run into tonight, no! I will put on my starving beggar disguise and only blow the boys who wish me well." You accept the good faith of foot queens, spade queens, trade queens, and fish queens, why pick on Socrates? He was a man who was sexually aroused by virtue in boys—not by black pearls of hair, ass like a pear, puckering nipples, tight boy balls are shifting, and the boy who has crawled underneath the sleeping man's cloak shifts so a

buttock will graze against Socrates' cock . . . no go . . . not a
stir in the long soft dick . . . I guess the boy isn't pure enough
inside. "There is no such thing as a bad boy," you are thinking, and maybe Socrates thought so too but he wouldn't
screw them till they showed up good more openly. Socrates
brought about virtue in his students by sexual induction—by
a huge erection visible through his gauzy marble gown
whenever a boy gave the right moral answer. And anyone
who has run into another human being with any strange new
sexual hunger whatsoever knows that the hunger immediately induces the means of satisfying it in the other party.
The desire of the Greek young men to be fucked made them
good.

There are more holy men around than you think. They
have infiltrated every trade and criminal profession. They are
vampires who refuse to stop sucking blood until they carry
all vampire-kind to a higher state of bliss. There is a bard
of goons and a saint of gimps and a tea-room queen and a
moral cop, and a saint of clubs and a peer of flips and a holy
flop in every crowd. There is a crooked shot and a master
creep and a saint of heads and the queen of feet, a thoughtful cunt, a lamb crank, a king of craps and the gong of prose.
Keep your eye on the glow in the still black rank, a star
gently prodding his flock up even higher in the empty space
—the herald—the Shepherd—the Hurrier!

One day the Master saw his disciples drive a mare away
with blows. "Stop!" he cried. "You are the beasts! Ach, how
can I be angry? You are moles or blind birds. This mare is
a woman, but your eyes are bewitched." After he spoke he
blew and blew and caused a mist to form, which gradually
rose. All those present saw La Maja naked where the mare
had stood. On another day the Master performed the bellows

pranayama with such amazing force that an actual tempest arose in the room. Then he extinguished his thundering breath. We sat motionless. The peace after the storm was vivid beyond forgetting.

He had risen several feet above ground and said, "I am sitting cross-eyed on a ridgepole of light in the flight of phenomena. Help me down." Anytime he gets a piece of crockery in his hands he floats to the ceiling and breaks it. He will do anything to get out of mess duty. St. Joseph of Cupertino was a seventeenth century levitating monk who was not permitted to serve breakfast. Silently in the morning thou fliest upward.

The numerous bodies that were spectacularly healed by the Master eventually fed the flames of the funeral pyre, but the quiet spiritual awakenings he effected are his imperishable miracles.

When I asked him if he ever compared his pupils' achievements with his own, he smiled and said, "Most of them have returned from journeys I will never venture in my life. They are my heroes."

"Can we build something greater than ourselves?" I asked.

"I accept only pupils wiser than I am," he said. "I see someone who can see farther than I, except his eyes jump. Mine are calm, and that's all he can learn from me."

The Master can look at any old schoolhouse, toilet, or cowbarn, and tell how many human orgasms have occurred there. He just stands there quietly, counting. He does it as a sort of parlor trick. He says they look like wobbly stars.

He is a shrivelled up monkey with English airs. His plus-fours were too baggy. He shat in them but now he wears a dhoti (diaper). He walks bowlegged to dry up the shit. His whole style is to keep one step ahead of his shit. Hear, hear.

Bibiji gave me a going-away gift of twelve exquisite photographs of the Master and a beautiful embroidered handkerchief. She asked me if I could use a thermos bottle. Hesitantly I whispered: "Yes!" Immediately the great Master directed that his fine and large thermos flask with shoulder carrying strap be given me. His generosity and loving detachment know no bounds.

Now this book will start squirming. If you wish to stop reading, this is the proper time to do so.

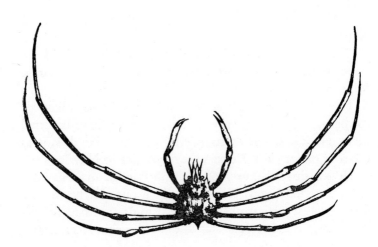

Part Seven

62

METAMORPHOSES

THIS IS SHEEPER speaking in the apple clearness of Vermont. Oi can't stand too close to the oil heater because moi cock is kind of big this morning down moi pant leg and gets burnt. Tother day oi chanced upon a young hermit on Blackbury Hill. He is against meat, violence, and civilization. He grows vegetables and saves all his shit—organic matter he calls it—for compost. He won't let a fart escape. First he retired to the woods some years back with his wife, and then he lost his wife. "She was out, and so I bathed and bandaged myself as well as I could, and then opened the knapsack to have another peek at my battle trophy. There to my horror and surprise was not the bear's forepaw but a bloody human hand—wearing her wedding ring." Ever since, he has abstained from meat and women. For clothes he scavenges a nearby village dump. "Just last week I found two shirts all bloody, somebody had a terrible accident. I washed them, now they're clean and nice. Amazing what the sun can do. . . . Let your hair grow, camerado. Don't cut your fingernails. Eat. Get fat. Save your shit. . . . Heck, all I buy in the store is cutie mags to jerk off with and I hope soon to drawr up my own. When I yen to touch of female flesh I eat a pound of prunes, the diarrhea turns me into a woman pissing, and there on the can I feel me up all

over. Funny I started out as a girl I guess everyone does,
running my hands on a giggling girl body all alone in bed
at night. Then the girl body sprouted. Fine hair in the groin
one day, and the cock too big to jerk off with a silver baby
cup the next. Did I join that ruddy boy's club called 'The
 Free Swingers'? Nix on that, I
rushed home after school to
strip and throw myself on the
bed pulling my genitals behind
me to be woman!—then suddenly open my legs to see the
whole body flow up into my cock on springs. Red giant cock
on a tiny white body. The clown cock is pulsing. And in my
mouth a cock crown gives off streams of flavor. Everything
changes. The celery I crunch, the glasses of ice cold milk and
soft egg salad sandwiches all turn into my hot body curled
in a fur cape. Smell the curly fur where it parts at the asshole. The celery which talks from the ground, the purple
turnip eyes up on the ground, these and all other vegetables
turn into shit and all fall down. However my anus opens and
closes like an iris diaphragm, the shit drops out perfectly, and
I never have to wipe myself—that's some compensation. On
successive wipes of toilet paper brown fades to ochre, but
Moslems say paper is uncouth and wipe themselves with
water. I am open to all philosophies including the Moslem
and profit from all. I blasted pot for two months and it
fucked up my mind. Couldn't think or do anything and had
to have help or go under. I walked the streets for two weeks
in a complete mental daze. Finally I walked into Bellevue, up
and down corridors and staircases, wards, courts, and waiting
rooms. I grabbed an elevator operator and made him take
me to the psycho ward. Six months and they let me go. I
walked the streets for two weeks in a complete mental daze.
Then some guy I had known down in Florida turned me on
one night and everything fell into place. A few years back

my body became so swollen that I had to wear extra large garments. Someone gave me a copy of *Science and Health*. I read the book through once and my body returned to its normal size. After studying Christian Science for some time, I realized that God's man has no false appetites, and I was healed of the marijuana habit. Recently I was stung on the head several times by wasps. I was able to know the truth so quickly and so firmly that there was not even any swelling. I know Hindoo truth and saw Krishna standing knife in hand at the little table by my stove. 'I am always incarnating,' he said chopping onions, 'how can I go beyond the ocean of this world?' 'O chop some more onions.' In the case of bad karma you go straight to the Niraya hell, painful in the extreme. In the case of naughty karma you go straight to the womb of a beast that skulks, quakes, or wavers, like a snake, skink, brown bunny or red-cheeked salamander, or any other animal that assumes a zigzag gait or hops on catching sight of a human being."

As an Englishman does not travel to see Englishmen, a fly does not travel to see flies. They have their own fly universe, to which they disappear right in front of your eyes. They flash in and out, from their world to ours. A fly will light on my leg when I am napping in the summer. I can scarcely muster the consciousness to brush it away. It was only a stray draft in the room tapping a hair. Or a hair springing free from crossing with another hair. Or it really was a fly, which is walking some distance from where I felt it, or has darted away. David gave me the strength to kill flies—and he kept me from seeping into the floor cracks. Where am I now? Study the floor. Love jells me and holds me together (I don't even notice the cracks) but David is at the opera with X. When Roy was in jail I made it with his Wife. O.K. I couldn't quite make it, so there in the sky above us where we lay fucking in horny violation of our eery bond, I gradually invoked the one I loved.

Apricot lions vomiting hideous roars and fires is how devils magically invoked at first appear. After several conjurations they slither from the greenish smoke as green and silver-sequined salamanders. Gradually they forsake these bestial shapes and grow more and more human, appearing after frequent repetition of the magic ritual as men of gentle countenance and sheeplike behavior. A pearl-handled pocket knife turns into a fish. Piercing a were-animal with a pocket  knife or bullet so that blood is drawn may force it to resume its human shape, but the stab should be on the brow between the eyes, and the bullet should be made of inherited silver and is all the better for having been blessed in a chapel of His Most Precious Blood. The idol of a friend of mine is blood. He always yells in at himself the same weary order: "Spirochaetes! Stop splashing in my blood like fish!" Then the crowns and mitres of Our Holiest Father appear in thin air—never in my life have I seen things more precious —and I am no superstitious peasant. I have been to Bohemia and many other places. And the battle of black shadows on the far wall as I put on my sweater is two big cats fucking, and yet everything is hushed by a soundproof window between them and me. My arms are struggling with the sweater. This (period). That (period). Piss (period).

Foot of a bat (period). To point silently with the inner finger.

Sometimes when a cockroach is stepped on and less often smashed on the wall, the elytra or outer wings are forced apart symmetrically, giving the body a triangular shape. I saw such a killed roach on the wall of my bathtub and thought, reaching for a piece of toilet paper, "My friends are conscientious in keeping down the vermin, but can't they wipe away the traces?" Before my hand touched the insect's body it fluttered into my face—a moth. Silently in the morning a house flies upward.

Moroccan boys screw each other with love and pleasure, and New York policemen sleep in the same bed. Screwing them later is like scraping toast. New York mice eat upturned roaches killed by spray—people are all interchangeable—insects turn into people. Or they turn into children smooth and bluish as Taka. "Taka" is Japanese for ladybird, an appropriate name for the daughter of so eminent an entomologist as is Mr. Nawa. She has  evidently inherited her father's love for the study of insects. Tea was served with candied locusts, crickets, dragonfly pupae, and other insects, which I sampled by sight only but which Mr. Nawa and his family ate with relish.

Two bugs came to life: "Hello, there. I am a gloom bug. I have very cute lamellae and my lover is a Mortuary Scientist. Can you guess what he brings me home from work to feed on?"

"Hello, there. My lover is a Porto Rican messenger. He wears dark glasses and smiles at bearded men. He scrawls 'Viva Fidel' on a wall of every elevator he is alone in. Whenever I am alone in an elevator I rape my mind between floors." Dammit I wish I had a happier disposition to hand down.

I don't like living!
I don't like it!
What's wrong with that?

Whine right. M.M. presses his damp lace handkerchief to
his forehead and whispers, "If you only knew what a torture
it is for me to live." For that we will change him into Sheeper's mother. Black brilliance to green flares, blue burning on
lavender, sparks of plum, smoke, bright pink flames, a brilliant opacity. Now listen to him: "If you only knew how
much I suffer, my gall bladder, my ovaries, and having to
live on one kidney, and not enough time to scrub the floor
every day with my swollen arms and legs—just look at them
fingers—how can I learn about music and reading books?
But you, I want you to learn everything I never had the
chance to learn. . . . That's why we bought you a violin." Let
me stop putting on M.M., my brother in too much stimulation. I browbeat him, I'm so ashamed of myself. I collect all
my screams and violent tendencies for a month and let them
loose in a letter to him. "Are you some kind of writer, pig, or
composer? Did you shave off your beard to see more?"
Therefore he sees me as a dragon (I hope and have a hard
time squaring this hope with my conscience). And I keep insisting I'm his brother. He steps back in fright. "What I saw
in the mirror when I shaved off my beard was the devil
sticking out his ass at me—motioning if I pulled down the
shade he'd show more!"

They say the devil's penis is a lizard. When my own lizard
vanished I searched the house for an hour trying to find him.
He was on my desk, motionless, directing my behavior. The
day he disappeared for good I had bought him a cup of
mealworms. I was at a loss what to do with them and let a
few crawl in my beard. Sally said, "Gosh, you'd be banned
anywhere." I kept them in a small black lacquered box, and

soon they turned into beetles eating each other up. In China pet crickets are kept in small fancy gourds with jade and ivory covers. The gourds are artificially shaped and figured, having been placed as flowers in tiny earthenware molds of every imaginable form and size, carved in intaglio. For centuries the Chinese have manufactured pearl idols by thrusting tiny metal armatures between the mantle and inner shell of oysters. These crystals dissolve and eat up the heat. And names like Huncke and Moltke send chills up a spine— and freeze me in feathers—till I crawl nude into the late autumn sun—Vermont. I see my own genitals for the first time in days. My cock is throbbing into my hand as I touch it, but I move it to one side. There is a huge patch of dead skin on my scrotum. I peel the patch off and look at it closely. It is a feather.

"Comrades! This session of the V.I. Lenin All-Union Academy of Agricultural Sciences has been a turning point in my life. I am a man of responsibility, for I am a member of the J.V. Stalin Prize Committee of the Council of Ministers, a professor at the Central Institute for the Further Qualification of Doctors, and chairman of the Committee of Experts on the Award of High Scientific Degrees. I therefore consider it my moral duty to disavow the erroneous views which I held until late last night and which I presented to the Academy in my paper three days ago. These views were contrary to the whole progressive spirit of Soviet biology as manifested in the patriotic work of our present chairman Trofim Denisovich and his great teacher I. V. Michurin. Also I want to apologize to the Academy for my behavior during Professor Dmitreyev's speech yesterday—which was pure ruffianism; I should have been ejected from the hall. Comrades I had a sleepless night. Your speeches rang through my mind. My brains were in a state of great disorder. Then, like a beam of light, an experience recalled from my own life taught me that I have been working in the darkness of a thoroughly incorrect biological and ideological theory. I don't mind telling you the experience, though it is very personal. Let me say that I offer it to you as a token of comradeship in the battle we must wage to liberate our biological sciences from the reactionary influence of Mendelism-Morganism. We must revise the obsolete textbooks and uproot this fruitless doctrine whenever it appears in our classrooms. The experience I recalled lying in bed is the edginess I have always felt on Christmas Day. I tie this edginess to my Jewish descent and I believe it to be a racial memory of pogroms. In other words, it is a characteristic acquired by my forebears, which I have inherited. Our Party has helped us to effect this profound and radical reconstruction of our science and has shown us conclusively that the Michurinian theory defines the basic line of development of Soviet biological science.

Last night I saw this all quite clearly.

"Comrades, I am sure that, knowing me, you will believe me when I say that it is not from cowardice that I have made this statement. One of the distinguishing features of my character, all through life, has been a deep impressibility. Everyone

knows how sensitively I react to everything. I cannot hold a
bottle of fruit flies up to the light without bursting into tears
—for the thousands I have slaughtered during the course of
my investigations. You can therefore believe me when I speak
of the impression all your speehes have made on me. They
have changed my whole life."

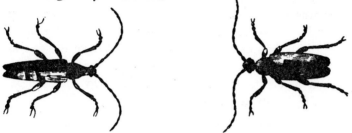

"One night a princess came to my door in an ebony car-
riage and asked me to dine with her. I accepted, and we
drove ten miles to a palace splendid beyond description.
She told me she had always loved me and asked if I would
stay with her forever, and I nodded. We lived in the fulfill-
ment of pleasure for years. One day a Buddhist priest bran-
dishing a cane suddenly entered the room of Her Highness.
Chamberlains and courtiers fled left and right. The priest
seized me and pushed me before him through a narrow passage between walls. He pushed me, pushed me, pushed me,
until I saw light, and found myself crawling from beneath
my own out-house." When the farmers heard this story, they
rushed to the out-house and demolished it, and as they did,
thirty or forty foxes wriggled out from below it and scattered
in all directions. Two foxes fleeing together took refuge in the
tomb of a king. After some weeks of rest they turned themselves into students with fine, open countenances, and engaged a learned priest in theological disputation over the
spirit of a memorial tree which stood before the tomb they
inhabited. The priest could not better them in argument and

said to himself, "Hee-hee ha-ha-ho hee-hee-hee they are spectres. Now hundred-year-old spectres show themselves when they see hounds, and thousand-year-old spectres when they see wood of the same age burning." So he set his dogs on them, but they showed not the slightest alarm. Then he sent a servant to fell the memorial tree. The spirit of the tree was a young child dressed in blue garments, sitting on a branch, and when he learned the tree would be felled, he wept bitterly and vanished. Blood oozed from the tree as it was chopped into. As soon as the wood was brought to the priest, he lit it, and as it kindled, the two youths became foxes racing away.

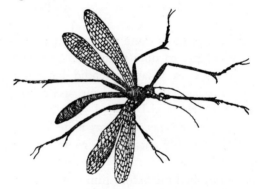

Ephemeroptera are May flies rotting to die in an hour, damsel flies stop in the air, blue needle quivers, pale hollow eyes, the head is the eyes, fly-hawks feed on Bombiliadae, the fly like a bee, elastic walking stick clings to a blue rock and the amateur entomologist creams in his jeans, use a number one pin prop it with cotton and the body shrivels and the legs break off, the Magic cicada has had her black wing veins sealed in plastic like an I.D. card, and does the great green hump of the katydid in a half cup of coffee—blue Danish stoneware in a glaring white kitchen—think of her buzzing grand dam electricity through high black wires of the night before, as I remember it was a damp night and I could hear the flutter of a bat like cloth unwrinkling.

And all day long a beautiful fly-hawk has been sunning itself on a clothesline outside my kitchen window, its wings moving in the wind. From a distance it is two rows of about a dozen gleaming white dots in the middle of the clothesline, so brilliant they blur and cannot be counted. Then it flies, like Utaemon dancing, to alight more close to me. Black and white spots splashed on glass, almost black and white stripes, parallel to the body and perpendicular to the wing, the black not black but deep brown. The wings vibrate and deflect in the breeze. A red metal flashes.

Seven P.M. in the corner of a glaring white laboratory. At a high black bench a man is standing, looking into a microscope, the lower part of his body squirming strangely. Dr. Ehrlich shoots into his hand and slices of brain submit to him. In a film laboratory Eisenstein shoots into a camera-like contraption of his own design and Marfa is splashed with cream. And who isn't sustained by visions of boys fucking, or fucking girls, or being fucked yourself, first your own cock kissed and nibbled, then a moving prick up your ass like bowels, and the pain pushing, pissing into pleasure, gently, he wants to give you, into the overwhelming pleasure of his body shuddering into your chest and mouth, sweet is his mouth. These faceless lovers do they ever appear? Who comes to your bed stealing through the window, is a burglar diverted? Is it a Mexican? A memory comes down on me, I showered and shaved and put on a new yellow shirt, and went to tell him that everything was cool, that I was over my crush or at least could control it, and wanted to be friends with him again, and wouldn't insist on touching him which led to our rupture, and he suddenly took me in his

arms while I stood in the doorway, God to this day I don't
know why, I had loved him and he said no. We were good
lovers for a year, he fucked me and unfucked me, and whatever art I have or love to give comes from a doorway, a spell
cast or broken, and in the bottom of my bureau drawer is a
yellow shirt with a small hole in its back, burned by an ash
that very afternoon, as he smoked in his easy chair, my head
resting on his belly, his cock hard under my chest. Eisenstein! Who laid you at Tetlapayac?

Part Eight

63

SCALES

BECAUSE Allen kisses me sweetly on arriving and departing.

Because he will use nocturnal pressures.

Because I dreamed up Ivan the Terrible Hipster.

Because the aroma of mental hospitals clings to my clothes.

Because I let a dog love my legs.

Because I see a fantastic bandage dance of gauze like chrysanthemums, of naked men turning into flowers and cold licking flames.

Because I see the instruments of torture and masturbation at my bedside.

Because I hold the green and white sweat shirt.

Because ego is written all over my fingers.

Because I envision the test tubes the fingers a candle the tongue of my wholly unreal and imaginary lover, who is bald and spectral.

Because I cannot read without masturbating.

Because I cannot turn on without masturbating.

Because I give myself marijuana treatments like a doctor.

Because I am meat.

Because I pull out my cock and look it square in the face.

Because an ant endlessly walks down the wall.

Because snow is yellow crystals where a dog pissed.

Because I sunshade my eyes.

Because I wear blinders when I walk.

Because when I let myself face a pair of eyes I am stabbed with longing.

Because I am smashed between: if you lie back you're just not responsive (you hate me), and: if you start fucking it's just to come off (you hate me).

Because one masturbation undermines all the fingers I stretch out to people. Rely on yourself, your fingers, your own stash of pot.

Because I am prepared to see plaster like glass or the heat that makes plaster unbearable.

Because I am the scales.

O I am the serpent! O I have the scales! The bright rosy scales! O I speak with the mouth of fishes! O I swim through the cold opal water! O I am Fish the Progenitor! By my bony scales!

Because I wave back the tide.

Because sometimes I start at the tip of my cock and run a finger down it all the way into my asshole.

Because I saw a rhinestone glimmering in the crack of pavement behind a man crawling to find it.

Because Huncke pissed in a man's mouth for money.

Because the man went gug gug gug and sucked for more piss which wasn't forthcoming as Huncke hadn't been able to keep from getting a hard-on. The great tide is stemmed.

Because no one is perfect.

Because Huncke's youthful beauty glimmers through his age and ugliness and thin wrinkles of his flesh like stars.

Because William Morris laid bread and pot on me when I was broke. Even though I put him down. Because much later he asked me for bread just to see if I would give it to him, as if his true heart's gift had been a loan. But still that gift glimmers!

Because I feel prickles in my ass and my piles are inviting my fingers.

Because if I had someone licking my asshole every night and therefore would be tempted to keep it in a condition of debris-less cleanliness I wouldn't keep thinking I had piles.

Because a friendly German shepherd rimming Melvin suddenly snarled "Gib mir etwas zu fressen oder ich fresse dich" and Melvin knew what he was talking about from previous chats and obliged. "I didn't give him very much, just a little little bit."

Because Huncke has laid pot on me many a time only to come back the next day and smoke it all up, only of course something always is left.

Because Ed Marshall went home with a sadist, who put a dog collar on him, stripped and said, "Fido, suck this!"

Because Ed Marshall smacked and slobbered with great canine gusto, and emitted yelps and growls of pleasure—thus degrading himself something awful, and him a poet and divinity student too.

Because that dog collar is silver and studded with black pearls and a magic opal, in which we see a black drake imprisoned—O shadowy opulence of flames and diamonds—smoke curling to Heaven—where eagles and elephants fly—skull on a reed and Eye in a hand—rapids of swirling water —a glass scarab falling down a stream of candleshine—bloody heads in the basket the Bird crows over—catskins and ratskins, Chinese claws, demon teeth on a belt—the emblems and banners—halo tongues squirming—the snakes are smiling—human bodies twist like whips in the paws of demon foxes—the opium She gives to the people—a flare of blue diamond sparkles—Kwan Yin!—It has to be so!

64

SCALES

BECAUSE in this book I rail against women but know there is no thing or creature in this strange world we find ourselves in that we are not bound to accept—"Thanks in the nose," I can hear them reply. Because the worth of my book is the distance between the lies in my art and the Truth in my eyes.

Because I am Gifted (poisoned by light).

Because my language is too precious to speak in.

Because I am come to Gehenna by spaceship.

Because women have a way of killing luster of the jewels they wear and blot out beauty by mechanical adorning.

Because the love seeps from my fingers. My love is the ink itself. Because the flame of anger in me has to keep burning whether I will it or no. Anything will feed it (all agents defect). The love and anger eat each other up.

Because making love in the dark for fear of showing my eczema makes me the prophet of skin. O I am the poet of language stretching out like a fan or panther foot!

O I am the great O poppy of U.S.A. prose! The nose and lips!

O the big eyes of love-you will burn you!

O I have an O inside me always surprised!

O this is it! The text! The bloom!

O get me off this fucking escalator! O great chronicle out of all time written! O great trunks of time! May I not be forgotten as long as cocks get hard! O centuries be kind! O give me restraint!

Because David and X left for New York to start a new life. In my heart I do bless them and wish them well—and thereby accumulate enough credits in Heaven I can murder a man.

Because I decided to live and so not kill myself or not kill myself and so live—which was it? In either case the margin of living was there—the memoir foreordained. I am on the side of life, but almost only as a fellow-traveller—truckless of this world and idiocy of propagation—glad to be always the foreigner.

Because the idea of two jazz musicians cutting each other —duelling instead of loving it up—puts me off, though jazz be real as things. You can hear the golden basketweave and there a burst of silver points. I guess one person with an alto sax can feel out another man blowing, exploring his sex with moist nervous fingertips—if only there were more of it. God keep some spider from changing all my record bands at night to make them say horrible things against me when I play them. I have stuck out two long bamboo tonguelike fingers into music, one into jazz and therefore another back into the classical music I had loved so much as a child and then given up sadly because I was the scales and could not keep myself attached to classical music remembering all the work it took me to dig it and not give jazz the same chance. Now I suppress all music with my long flat fingers, and leave these interplanetary battles drift in the ether, and hie me to Morocco, where all sound will slay me.

Because the false tooth never gets yellow.

Because I see more flaws in this book than any man will ever after.

Because I read for style alone. For style and sex, I admit it, and comb long badly written manuscripts looking for sex, and make it with men I don't dig, a rather grave sin I believe. But thank Heaven Huncke makes up for neurotic intolerance and does it one better: "Even in my briefest encounters as a hustler and male prostitute, I always enjoyed the mental contact as well."

Because my brain served me well in that it made me High Floating Cream, on the other hand it keeps letting itself be used to obstruct the flow of bone milk. Something else would have come to hand? But brain did and now we mush it up. My mother used to purée cooked apples with a conical mortar in a conical sieve. "When you were little I used to paray all your food for you." She drops that remark in company. She neglects to mention how she parayed it—by chewing, in her own mouth, thus feeding me her poisons. Hand me the parayer.

Because I am hurling burning powder on the page like a god—with my fucking gold fingernails—and letting out farts my mother called poops. Sing O doctor of thorns and interiors—and poppy of U.S.A. prose—more and more young puppy ways in which farts can be let—O snout and lips!

Because my young cousin farts, he is a lamb, and I like him anyway. Burbling farts tickle his ass in the bathtub. "The bubbooes tickoo me," he laughs.

Because whenever I wash my ass with Red Roses soap, no matter how well I rinse out the washcloth it still has a fanny smell.

Because in the morning the Mexican would wash me off his body (I could sense the shower running and no warm legs to place my leg between as if by accident of sleep), while I would keep the precious smell and semen of his body on my skin as long as I could. Later on I would awake in his smell though he was gone, and in the afternoon when I was at a lecture taking notes, sometimes an unexpected whiff of him would come up from my own chest as I turned a page, and I would excuse myself, go out into the hall and bunch up my shirt to smell it, and walk in a little circle drunk on his odor.

O I wore his love like a rhinestone ring, for my flesh not to break out in diamonds!

Because I snatched the magic ring of spit from the mouth of Mohammed ben Abdullah Yussufi and by jolt of eyeshine forced it to complete itself and glow—and saw the dark forehead sprayed or starred or streaked with light. By my Jewish stars! By my eyes!

Because Mohammed ben Abdullah's eyes were big and black and Persian—and fixed on immense treasures hid from common view, I would say from his parallax no more than ten yards away, and he could be wheedled out of a gem or two, if he was cross-legged and quiet with the mint tea boiling on a charcoal *mizmar,* those cold Tangier nights when only magic spells can drive away the damp.

Because he was a failure in his chosen profession. "A Socco hustler without any force—I do not solicit, I never speak to strangers unless spoken to first, I never ask people to buy me so much as a glass of coffee, I never sit at anyone's table without being invited, and I never look straight into anyone's eyes, for I know my place, it is very low, I am like the fleas I rub between my fingers. And when I sit with others I sit with my eyes down and head bent. And ears up like fingers." He told me that he never killed fleas, but I caught him rubbing one between his fingers apparently to stun it as my father used to do before crushing it between his fingernails. "I thought you never kill fleas," I chid. "I don't," he said, dropping the live insect into an ash tray. "But I break their legs so they will know a little of the suffering they cause me." And he sighed like a Jew and rolled up his eyes.

Because when I, not to be outdone in self-pity, showed him the scar on my left little finger cut by a bottle-opener my mother threw at me one day, he showed me the burn scars on his eyelid and forehead from a *mizmar* his father had thrown in his face. By my stars! By my eyes!

The eyes! The eyes! It is known that many persons with two eyes see darkly. An ingenious device has just been discovered for filling the whole body with light. May white wine drip from the mouths of our horses.

Because on or about December 30, 1963, the young Moroccan poet Mohammed ben Abdullah Yussufi was beaten to death by the Tangier police. Had he lived he would have shone down great honor on Morocco.

Because I myself was arrested on a trumped-up charge of passing counterfeit money, but my only crime was in knowing Mohammed ben Abdullah and in knowing how he died.

Because I saw other prisoners—Moroccans—young kids like Mohammed—being beaten down to the floor with a belt buckle. Some cried, some didn't. And sometimes I think of one with the same soft Persian manner of Mohammed, except he loved to be beaten and did what he could to provoke the cops. And he screamed bloody murder when the beating took place, and the Man drooling slightly hit him even harder—and with every thwack and scream you could hear the quiet rustle of the belt buckle lashing upward in the empty space. A half hour later the boy was fresh and calmly cleaning his fingernails, he had got his rocks off for the day. As karmas go, that was the saddest I saw in Morocco.

Because a Chinese is able to stand crickets screaming for any length of time.

Because Death arms her shadows, and turns oppressive thoughts to dragons, brass gorgons, or gryphons they say, but not for me. I love beaky monsters so much I wish some would haunt me.

Because what haunts or shatters soon is grey and feathered.

Because familiarity feathers. And, alas, the horrible beautiful insects scattered all through these pages by now are as dear and familiar as tinkly-belled cats or as stupid as chickens. Once I said I would rather sleep with a handsome insect than a boy with turgid lips, but not any more. Still I love everything winged and scaled and slow-moving when it can strike like a hammerblow.

Dream! star! insect! are all of the same luminous cloth. But the word insect is invested with such cranny horror (who put it there?) that we don't see the word, rather we hear it spoken by an old man with perfect white chompers to scare you. Don't pay any attention to him. He is an Ugliness Trap—shyer of beauty than a damp white root. Everything lacquered he sees he wants to coat with the fat floating in dishwater. O keep your eye on the mantises preening themselves.

All animals are my life, the beauty always twisting, little

green frogs, green sequin beetles, sweet trembling antennae, the squirming in crevices, warm young homo tongues slip into crevices, sand crabs in the hand, the black pull of Reese who is a Negro, Negroes pull skeletons out from the slime, slime weaves with hysterical worms farting, belching, and giggling at once, numerous skeletons sit up to read New York Times summer camp ads pulsing with young boy, we could hold roaches for Michael this beautiful young sweet panting animal I think a deer-hound cub, see the high Gothic mantis in graceful court dancing with craneflies on the floor who cannot fly with their balance organs amputated, silly.

O peek into my death's-head. I left the lamp on for you. See the Turkish saddle. See the Gothic bones.

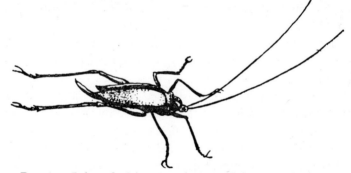

Because I loved the Poet skull and bones—for months and months—when he was insane. I tried to lure him back to the living.

Because just when I was winning, his mother stuck him back in the hospital.

Because a vague consciousness of my love came back to him 175 shock treatments later, and he tried, cautiously, to fly in on my love stream. "Poet to Sheeper, over. Poet to Sheeper, over." The love was healed over.

Because nothing is lost. For if you partial out what there is of Charles in the work of the Poet, he comes right up through that lard with his own fat crackling. Yet we love the way he cherishes the line he learned from Charles, and we love the imperfections of his imitation, which are his alone. The conceit of Charles's line burned out by innocence. And if this hollow line dies, as it will, at least the Poet's deathmask of it will survive.

Because they have flooded the Poet's brain with insulin—mad tampering doctors, the coughers and scoffers that feed off of minds—and his Art will prevail. Because they have filled up the Parthenon with gunpowder, but the hand of Ictinus shapes the doorposts of Nashville. The mud in our minds settles on standing, and our dreams supernatant pre-vail. What is harder than diamond is mind. It will prevail.

Go spend twenty-five years hammering and chiselling your mind into order and see what you have. I will tell you. A young-looking science student, a bit over-fed, making oh such pithy remarks about politics and chess to a girl science student at a party where drinks are served in wax cups. He is wearing a tie. He holds up his wrist so that she can read his identification bracelet. It says something like Mervin F. Finkelstein. He has erotic thoughts. Hup! I can describe him another way. While thumbing through the Scientific American he has thoughts like this: "Yummy! Mathematical puzzles." No, no, no, you have to start all over—dissolve out the order with pot. A trace of it will remain, a pure golden honeycomb eaten away. The skull turned to gold. What you see in the nose hole: I hate colons, if you must know the perpendicular process of the ethmoid, the bony septum, in cats turned to Viennese pastry, but gold, a bright foil struc-ture too fragile to touch. Or let it form in eons of granite pressure till it shines. The mind is a diamond.

Because the Poet wrote "I come to the last defense." Because this last defense was the love made pure. He sorted mail so his lover could go to school. "I worked my ass off, and for what?" he told me in private. He made all that pass under, the shit and bickering, the begrudging—when he wrote he distilled out the love. It is there, the love, only on the page become pure. And I bowed down before him, as he had bowed down to love, because at first I thought his love was pure, as in the poem. His broken nose, what of the blackheads now? His youthful beauty glimmered through his age and ugliness and thin wrinkles of his flesh like stars. I studied his face. And now in it I saw malice and vanity— he is just like the rest of us, I was shocked to discover it. Gloom and disappointment shook in my arms like black spaniels. Then in my brains a trickle of light, his art, a Light, a triumph of art, and all at once his glamour came back to me streaming. For to have loved purely, that is great, and I was correct to have bowed down before it if I saw it. But to have loved badly, which is our lot, and to have made that love live pure in the poem, that is great too and crooked like our fingers.

65

SCALES

BECAUSE in Beverly Hills I saw a silver blonde with a white wool stole around her head and in Life Magazine a Colombian squaw grinning from a black shawl and fedora—I put down the Indian who prefers his wife to Lana Turner. Let him screw the stars and not settle for the comfortable homeliness of his native village. Let him chew coca and screw stars.

Because I saw big cakes of broken chocolate at the candy store, but because I saw that these cakes were *white*, white chocolate, and I bought half a pound, and I saw another kind, pale brown chocolate, and I wasn't satisfied with white ant chocolate, the miracle of it, and bought half a pound of pale brown chocolate expecting some miraculous mocca-cacao taste, as the white chocolate tasted vanilla, tasted chocolate in every way but flavor—but the pale brown chocolate was butterscotch, and I walked home with a bag of mixed white and pale brown chocolate, hating the butterscotch flavor. To discover the white chocolate did I have to suffer the butterscotch?

Because I took peyote and suffered the fear of death creeping into my legs and heart, shaking into them, and this fear was met by a delicious Plant security, manifesting itself in wave after wave of honey glowing into my blood and lymph —relax, relax.

Because when I faced Allen under ether I saw he loved me exceedingly, but my facing him stopped that love in its tracks, built a wall around it that will never be scaled.

Because everything I get and love is spoiled. But I am left with something, I can't say what, something remains, a trace, a taste of vanilla chocolate, honey in the blood, left pure, a memory left pure, an uprush of Light, the swell of carnations, a small white skull, perhaps of a child or monkey.

A residuum, a line of dry foam on the beach, an infinitesimal profit. And perhaps the only profit is the words themselves, so many, an ugly accretion with no special separate power or strident outside beauty, as if I were a man standing in a quartz cave to whom a taper has been given but whose way is hid, and he walks along the Golden Lode filling page after page with detailed scientific notes. But his ball-point pen ran out of ink before he ever began. Yet he vainly reassures himself with memories of his papers, degrees, and employments. "And this—" he cries out, holding up his notebook, "this is it. The text. The bloom." He sits on the hard prickly quartz, all cones and spikes. At home, where it is warm, the deathwatch beetles would be ticking in the woodwork. He sticks the taper into a translucent fissure protected from drafts, and the cold and quaking light subsides. Finally he lies down, using for a pillow his open notebook, the pages springy with invisible writing. The candleflame is small, pure, and absolutely still.

O all these gold ribbons blowing with the rhythm of breathing, breathe in, breathe out, the Light falls quite gently now, breasts heaving, red blood become milk.